national health council presents

270 WAYS

TO PUT YOUR TALENT TO WORK IN THE HEALTH FIELD

National Health Council

The Council would like to give special thanks for its generous support of this publication to the Health Resources and Services Administration, U.S. Department of Health and Human Services.

NATIONAL HEALTH COUNCIL

The National Health Council (NHC) is a private, nonprofit association of national organizations which was founded in 1920 as a clearinghouse and cooperative effort for voluntary health agencies (VHAs). Today, these agencies remain the core of the Council, which works to promote and strengthen the movement they embody. VHAs improve health by providing patient and family services, community services, public and professional education, medical research support, and health-related advocacy.

The many contributions of the Council's VHA members exemplify the voluntary health movement. They fill gaps in service that might not otherwise be met, making these valuable contributions with the generous support of volunteers and the donating public. With a strong sense of human concern, these agencies provide unique and indispensable services to individuals and families of people with debilitating and life-threatening illnesses, chronic health conditions and other physical, mental and developmental disabilities.

The NHC promotes responsible and effective VHA leadership and accountability, as well as cooperation among a broad array of national health-related organizations. To foster needed communication and collaboration among the diverse organizations comprising the health community, the Council expanded its membership in the 1960's to include health-related professional and membership associations, nonprofit organizations, businesses, and federal government agencies.

MISSION The National Health Council's mission is to promote the health of all people by advancing the voluntary health movement. This movement is driven by volunteers who, as individuals, families, and communities, work together toward the prevention, treatment and cure of disease and disability.

VISION National Health Council members share a vision of a caring society of healthy individuals and communities that enjoy the virtues of health education and disease prevention and the benefits of effective medical, behavioral and health services research advances.

Council members share a vision of a public widely and actively engaged in volunteerism and charitable giving in support of the vital role played by the nation's voluntary health agencies.

Council members share a vision of a health system which offers universal access to the full continuum of appropriate services, improves health status measurably, and promotes continued medical progress. Additionally, this system would respect human dignity, foster individual responsibility, and enhance quality of life for all.

TABLE OF CONTENTS

INTRODUCTION

270 Ways to Put Your Talent To Work in the Health Field is a reference guide designed to help students, guidance counselors, parents or anyone considering a career in the health field. This newly revised and updated edition is far more comprehensive than previous versions; it includes an expanded list of careers and more extensive information on each. It also includes, for the first time, sections on careers in alternative medicine and health careers in the military.

Each major category (shown in bold throughout the publication) provides an overview of information about that category. Included within each major category are listings (shown in italics) of specific professions and areas of specialization, where applicable. These listings include career descriptions, educational requirements, and salary and job outlook (for some categories, no salary information was available).

At the end of each entry is a listing of health associations that provide career-specific information, such as listings of training schools and programs, financial aid programs, and job listings. Users will find a comprehensive index in the back of this guide that provides the addresses, phone and fax numbers, Internet addresses, and E-mail addresses for more than 120 of these organizations.

270 Ways has been in print for more than twenty years and has been used by more than four million students and advisors.

Special thanks to Bob Goldberg, VP, Operations & Membership, National Health Council, for his efforts in leading the research, development, editing and marketing of this publication. Thanks also to Dee Ellison, Director of Communications, for her oversight of this project, and to Susan Jane Adamcik for her efforts in researching and compiling the information.

SOURCE AND ASSUMPTIONS

The career information, unless cited otherwise, was obtained directly from the United States Bureau of Labor Statistics. Projections about the outlook of specific health careers were based on the assumption of moderate future economic growth, increased productivity, and a fairly constant unemployment rate. Spending on health care was predicted to grow faster than average. These projections are by no means certain, but represent a likely scenario based on the reports and opinions of educated professionals.

DOCTORAL DEGREE

        Biological scientists

        Medical scientists

MASTER'S DEGREE

        Speech-language pathologists and audiologists

        Psychologists

BACHELOR'S DEGREE

        Occupational therapists

        Physical therapists

ASSOCIATE'S DEGREE

        Medical records technicians

        Dental hygienists

        Respiratory therapists

        Cardiology technicians

POSTSECONDARY VOCATIONAL TRAINING

        Emergency medical technicians

        Surgical technologists

        Medical secretaries

1-12 MONTHS OF ON-THE JOB/INFORMAL TRAINING

        Physical and corrective therapy assistants and aides

        Medical assistants

        Occupational therapy assistants and aides

        Social and human services assistants

UP TO A MONTH OF ON-THE-JOB/INFORMAL TRAINING

        Personal and home care aides

        Home health aides

Source: Bureau of Labor Statistics, 1998

For hospitals and other medical facilities, the clinical laboratory serves as an invaluable diagnostic center that employs highly trained professionals of all types. *Cytotechnologists, histologic technicians and histotechnologists, medical technologists, medical laboratory technicians, phlebotomists,* and *specialists in blood bank technology* constitute the core staff of any clinical laboratory and interact daily with health care providers and administrators.

Laboratory personnel perform specialized tests on blood, other bodily fluids, and tissue samples to detect disease, infection, and chemical imbalances in patients. In modern health care facilities these diagnostic tests are as important as ever, and advances in technology and medicine have increased their accuracy and application. Clinical laboratory professionals are expected to successfully make the shift from a hospital laboratory to an independent laboratory in the upcoming years, and to make greater use of computers and automated equipment within the laboratory.

A career in a clinical laboratory is exciting, rewarding, and offers the opportunity to make discoveries that help save patients' lives.

CYTOTECHNOLOGIST

Description: Cytotechnologists (CTs) are medical technologists who study cells and cellular abnormalities. They use the microscope to screen slides of human cells to detect if cancerous or precancerous cells are present. By observing the stained nuclei and cytoplasmic structures within individual cells, cytotechnologists can identify malignancies. Cytotechnologists may catch a disease at a treatable stage and thus directly aid in extending a patient's life. Cytotechnologists work independently to evaluate and report on normal cells, or work with a pathologist to study cancerous or abnormal cells.

Cytotechnologists may practice in numerous settings. Hospital and private laboratories provide excellent opportunities, as do public health facilities, clinics, medical schools, federal institutions, and research/industry facilities. Full-time as well as part-time positions are available, and hours range from around-the-clock in hospitals to standard business hours elsewhere.

Education: Training programs in cytotechnology exist at the baccalaureate and post-baccalaureate certificate levels. Usually, students are accepted into an accredited hospital or university-based program after their junior year of college and enroll after graduation. Training may last from one to two years and confers eligibility to take the national certification exam offered by the American Society of Clinical Pathologists (ASCP). If the exam is passed, the individual is then identified as a CT(ASCP). Individuals who have not completed an accredited training program may still seek certification if they have at least five years of experience and a baccalaureate degree.

Salary, Future Outlook: Cytotechnologists earned $18 an hour in 1996. This salary is competitive with that of most other allied health professionals and should grow over time. Regional factors and years of experience also contribute to earnings potential.

Experienced independent cytotechnologists will be needed in laboratories over the next decade. As new screening and identification techniques for cancer are developed, cytotechnologists will be an invaluable resource. Over time, there may be a decreased need for cytotechnologists in hospitals, as outside laboratories assume the bulk of diagnostic analyses. In addition, routine techniques may be simplified to a point where specific training is no longer necessary.

Index: *American Society for Clinical Pathologists, American Society of Cytopathology, American Society for Cytotechnology, Commission on Accreditation of Allied Health Education Programs, International Society for Clinical Laboratory Technology*

HISTOLOGIC TECHNICIAN AND HISTOTECHNOLOGIST

Description: Histologic technicians (HTs) and histotechnologists (HTLs) are clinical laboratory workers who prepare body tissues for microscopic examination by pathologists (medical doctors specializing in tissue disease). A microtome[1] is used by histology workers to cut a thin cross-section of biopsied tissue which, when stained, will show signs of abnormality, illness, or disease. Histologic technicians perform such tasks as sectioning and staining tissues, embedding tissues in paraffin or plastic, preparing frozen sections of tissues directly from the operating room, and operating intricate equipment including microscopes and microtomes. Histotechnologists perform all of the tasks of a technician and more complex procedures as well. They may do analyses of sample histochemistry, explore immunological links to disease, prepare samples for electron microscopy, or supervise and teach others. Both careers are vital to the early detection of disease and illness.

Histologic technicians and technologists primarily work in hospital and independent laboratories as well as in clinics, public health facilities, forensic medicine facilities, and in industrial research. Government agencies, pharmaceutical companies, and universities may also hire histology personnel. The majority of technicians and technologists work full time, and a 40-hour work week may include shifts at night, on weekends, and during holidays.

Education: Qualifying for histologic technician certification requires a high school diploma. Additional requirements include completion of an accredited HT training program, or two years of laboratory experience. The 31 training programs currently available in the USA are generally hospital- or university-based and last from one to two years. For those with an associate's degree, only one year of experience is necessary. An associate's degree is a definite advantage and is required for more complex duties. Histologic technologists must have a baccalaureate degree; the completion of an accredited HTL training program or a year of experience is also required. Currently, there are three accredited training programs in the United States. The American Society of Clinical Pathologists conducts the certification examination for these two careers and will award the designation HT(ASCP) or HTL(ASCP) to those who pass.

Salary, Future Outlook: In 1996, histologic technicians earned a minimum of $10.70 an hour and an average $13.50 an hour. Histotechnologists earned two to three thousand dollars more annually due to their extra training and specialized services. Earnings varied due to skill level, location, and years of experience.

Although advances in medical technology will aid laboratory accuracy and increase work volume, these same advances may replace technicians and technologists with computers or robots. Like other laboratory employees, histologic technicians and histotechnologists will have more employment opportunities in independent laboratories and research facilities than in hospital laboratories. Most job openings in both fields will be due to workers exiting the field and leaving vacancies; applicants with clinical experience will be in demand.

Index: *American Society of Clinical Pathologists, International Society for Clinical Laboratory Technology, National Society for Histotechnology*

---

[1] An instrument used to cut a specimen, such as organic tissue, into thin sections for microscopic examination.

MEDICAL LABORATORY TECHNICIAN

Description: Medical laboratory technicians (MLTs) are clinical laboratory personnel who perform a variety of tests under the supervision of a medical technologist. They aid in the detection, diagnosis and treatment of disease and accomplish this through specific tasks, including inoculating culture media, performing microscopic evaluations, and operating high-tech equipment. MLTs perform routine tests in the areas of blood banking, chemistry, hematology, immunology, microbiology and urinalysis - an experienced MLT will be familiar with all of these areas. **Histology technicians** and **phlebotomists** also fall into the category of MLTs and are described in detail elsewhere.

While laboratory personnel are always present in hospitals, other employment sites include physicians' offices, clinics, research facilities, federal agencies, managed care organizations (MCOs) and pharmaceutical companies. Because MLTs have general knowledge of a wide range of science fields, they are used in a variety of settings. A 40-hour work week is common, and the hours may be distributed over evening shifts or weekends.

Education: Most medical laboratory technicians first receive an associate's degree from a community or junior college, or a certificate from hospital or vocational-technical school. There are close to 400 accredited training programs for clinical laboratory scientists and they include academic preparation and clinical experience. Once the educational requirements are met, an individual may attempt a certification examination offered by the American Medical Technologists (AMT) to earn the designation MLT(AMT). Promotion from a medical laboratory technician position to medical technologist is a likely progression in this field.

Salary, Future Outlook: In 1997, the minimum average salary for medical laboratory technicians was $23,700 with the median closer to $27,000. For all clinical laboratory workers, the average was closer to $27,000. The relatively lower salary earned by MLTs is indicative of the fact that they require less training and are less specialized. Earnings may vary by location, years of experience, and work setting.

Medical laboratory technicians can expect average job growth for the next decade. Like all laboratory workers, MLTs will be helped as well as hurt by new advances in medical technology. Automated and simplified procedures and equipment threaten to eliminate the need for specialized laboratory personnel, although innovations are likely to generate an increase in laboratory workload. MLTs with the highest degree of training are likely to still be in demand.

Index: *American Medical Technologists, American Society of Clinical Pathologists, International Society for Clinical Laboratory Technology*

MEDICAL TECHNOLOGIST

Description: Medical technologists (MTs) are clinical laboratory technologists who serve in a supervisory role to medical laboratory technicians. MTs may perform a wide range of tests in all areas of science or may choose to focus their skills in one area. For example, *clinical chemistry technologists* conduct tests on blood and bodily fluids with respect to their chemical characteristics, *microbiology technologists* specialize in micro-organisms and bacteria, *blood bank technologists* maintain and evaluate blood supplies and *immunology technologists* focus on the immune system and its functions. **Cytotechnologists** and **histotechnologists** also fall into the category of medical laboratory technologists and are explained elsewhere. MTs must be proficient in microscopy and other laboratory procedures because they almost always work without direct supervision.

The majority of medical technologists are employed by hospitals, although opportunities also exist in independent laboratories, physicians' offices or clinics, research laboratories, or federal agencies. Working conditions and hours worked per week depend upon the work setting, although most MTs are full-time employees. Some technologists may work shifts during weekend, evening or holiday hours, and some may be on call to attend to emergency situations.

Education: The first requirement for becoming a certified medical technologist is a bachelor's degree in a related science. In addition, the degree-holder must either enroll in an accredited MT program or, alternatively, already be a certified medical laboratory technician with three years' experience, or have five years' clinical laboratory experience. If these prerequisites are met, certification may be sought from the American Medical Technologists, which awards the designation MT(AMT). A master's degree in medical technology is available to MTs interested in teaching in administrative positions.

Salary, Future Outlook: In 1997, medical technologists earned a minimum salary of $26,033 and a median salary of $35,100. While medical technologists with advanced training tend to earn more, employment setting, geographic location, and experience are also factors.

For medical technologists, job growth is likely to be average in coming years. Most job openings will occur as individuals leave the profession, and the number of new openings will be determined by progress in medical technology. While some innovations will increase laboratory workload, others will reduce the number of personnel required for laboratory procedures. Advanced training will increase employment opportunities and jobs in independent laboratories are likely to be most abundant.

Index: *American Association for Clinical Chemistry, American Medical Technologists, American Society for Clinical Laboratory Science, American Society of Clinical Pathologists, American Society for Microbiology, International Society for Clinical Laboratory Technology*

PHLEBOTOMIST

Description: Also known as registered phlebotomy technicians (RPTs), phlebotomists are medical laboratory technicians whose primary role is to collect blood samples directly from the patient. Using safe and minimally painful techniques, the phlebotomist draws blood via venipuncture and keeps careful records of all procedures. Blood may be collected for work in a clinical laboratory or may be drawn for blood bank collection. Safety precautions are of utmost concern to phlebotomists owing to the nature of their work.

Phlebotomists may be employed in hospital laboratories, blood banks, blood donation centers, doctors' offices, clinics and nursing homes. In hospitals, phlebotomists may be needed around the clock, while other settings may be more conducive to typical business hours. Full-time as well as part-time employment is possible.

Education: In addition to a high school diploma, interested individuals should also be enrolled in an approved phlebotomy program, a formal structured training program, or have one year of experience in a laboratory setting. American Medical Technologists conducts the certification examination and awards the Registered Phlebotomy Technician title.

Salary, Future Outlook: In 1996, phlebotomists earned the least of any clinical laboratory technician. The minimum wage earned by a phlebotomist was $7.00 an hour and the median was $8.50 an hour, data may differ depending on experience, location, and employer.

Although clinical laboratory servers will see only average growth in the next decade, phlebotomists will always be needed to draw patients' blood. With the advent of modern diagnostic testing, blood will be even more vital in disease detection, although automation and robotics may reduce some of the demand for phlebotomy technicians.

Index: *American Medical Technologists, International Society for Clinical Laboratory Technology*

SPECIALIST IN BLOOD BANK TECHNOLOGY

Description: Specialists in blood bank technology are medical technologists with advanced training needed for blood bank techniques such as typing, collection, and transfusion. Specialists in blood bank technology also search for blood irregularities and are responsible for processing, testing, and labeling donor blood. Disease control is a priority for these specialists because they ensure that blood samples are safe for public use and are handled properly. It is important for specialists in blood bank technology to minimize their risk of exposure as they come in direct, daily contact with blood.

Hospitals employ the majority of blood bank technology specialists. Other opportunities may exist in community or university blood bank centers, laboratories, and government agencies. The number of hours worked and shifts available depend upon the place of employment. Hospital blood bank workers may need to be on call or fill round-the-clock shifts, while some blood centers and government jobs may operate on regular business hours. Full-time and part-time positions are available.

Education: Similar educational and training requirements exist for all of the careers in clinical laboratory specialization. Once at the graduate level, technologists may gain admission to a specialization program via one of three routes: five years of experience in addition to a bachelor's degree and medical technologist certification; four years of experience along with a master's degree; or a doctorate degree with two years of experience. Training programs last over a year and are offered by hospitals and colleges. Upon completion, graduates may sit for a certification examination given by the American Society of Clinical Pathologists.

Salary, Future Outlook: For clinical laboratory technologists and technicians as a whole, the median annual earnings were $26,500 in 1997. The extra training and skills of specialists in blood bank technology allow them to earn more than laboratory technologists.

Expect average growth for specialists in blood bank technology in the near future. With the advent of new procedures and equipment in blood banking, more laboratory workers will be needed to oversee and operate them. However, these innovations may ultimately speed up, simplify, and computerize current laboratory practices to such an extent that fewer people are needed. Medical laboratories are likely to provide more job opportunities than hospitals, as blood work is sent to outside facilities with increasing frequency.

Index: *American Association of Blood Banks, American Medical Technologists, Commission on Accreditation of Allied Health Education Programs, International Society for Clinical Laboratory Technology*

DENTISTRY

Dentistry is one of the most respected fields in health care today. The *dentist* is the head of a team of professionals which includes the *dental assistant, dental laboratory technician,* and *dental hygienist.* The dental team not only treats diseases of the teeth and mouth, they also focus on preventive dental care and patient education.

Patients today are more concerned with dental health than ever before, and are also opting for more cosmetic dental procedures. Increasingly, dental practices are becoming affiliated with health maintenance organizations (HMO's) rather than remaining as private solo or group practices. In another trend, dental assistants, technicians and hygienists are assuming more of the responsibilities in expanding dental practices because their services are more affordable.

Dentistry has a promising future and is a growing health care field. Dental professionals achieve prestige, financial stability, and unlike most workers, actually see their hard work reflected in the smiles of satisfied patients.

DENTIST

Description: Dentists (DDS, DMD) detect, diagnose, and treat problems affecting the teeth, gums, tongue, lips and jaws. In addition, they advocate preventive dental care by teaching their patients brushing, flossing, and dietary techniques. As part of their wide range of duties, dentists identify and fill cavities, repair any dental damage or breakage, analyze X-rays, and may also prescribe medication or administer anesthetics. Cosmetically, dentists may improve patients' appearance through corrective surgery to the gums and mouth cavity, making use of modern dental equipment. A dentist in private practice must also carry out the administrative duties that any business requires, including hiring personnel. The majority of dentists choose to be general practitioners but the following eight specialty areas do exist: *endodontists* (perform root canal therapy), *oral and maxillofacial surgeons* (operate on facial and oral structures), *oral pathologists* (study and diagnose diseases of the mouth), *orthodontists* (straighten teeth and align jaws), *pediatric dentists* (specialize in children's dentistry), *periodontists* (treat gum disease), *prosthodontists* (replace teeth with artificial ones or dentures), and *dental public health* (exercise community-wide control of dental health).

Education: Approximately 90% of dentists engage in an office-based private practice while others may work in hospitals, clinics or research laboratories. A 40-hour work week is typical, with hours set to accommodate patients' schedules. While solo practice is most common, group practices or partnerships do exist.

A pre-dental student's education is science based and while a minimum of two years of college is sufficient for dental school admissions, a bachelor's degree is recommended. The Dental Admissions Test (DAT) is required for admission and will allow the student to engage in four years of academic and clinical work at an accredited dental school. A Doctor of Dental Surgery (DDS) or equivalent Doctor of Dental Medicine (DMD) degree will be awarded upon graduation. State and National Board exams must also be passed for full licensing. Specialization may require two to four more additional years of study and additional exams, depending on the state of practice.

Salary, Future Outlook: For 1995, the American Dental Association listed the earnings of a private practice dentist at $120,000 a year on average with specialists at the higher end of the scale at $175,000 per year, and general practitioners at the lower end at $109,000 per year.

In 1996, there were 162,000 dentists in the United States. Although new dentists will be needed to fill the spots of retirees, employment is not expected to surpass the national average for occupations in the next ten years. While dental care will still be in demand due to an increasing elderly population, dental practices are expected to rely more on dental assistants and hygienists to manage their workload.

Index: *American Association of Dental Schools, American Association of Orthodontists, American Dental Association, National Dental Association*

DENTAL ASSISTANT

Description: Dental assistants perform a wide range of tasks that may be interpersonal, technical or administrative. They expose and develop X-rays, coordinate and implement infection control protocols, take diagnostic impressions, maintain inventory control, perform numerous office management tasks, and assist the dentist with equipment at chair-side. Dental assistants often interact with patients and may provide preventive dental instruction, or tend to the patient's comfort.

The majority of dental assistants are employed by dentists in private solo or group practices. Other work locations include dental schools or public health clinics, civil and military services, hospitals or even insurance companies. Dental assistants work on a team with dental hygienists and dentists and often work close to 40 hours a week; approximately 30% are part-time workers.

Education: On-the-job training is the most popular method of skill acquisition for dental assistants. Training programs are also offered by community colleges, vocational schools, technical institutes, or universities; there were 235 accredited programs in 1995. One-year program enrollees receive a certificate or diploma upon completion, while those in two-year programs finish with an associate's degree. Although not mandatory for employment, certification is an option for training program graduates or for those with two full years of experience.

Salary, Future Outlook: Full-time dental assistants reportedly earned an average of $361 a week in 1996.

In 1996, dental assistants occupied 202,000 jobs. Entry-level positions will be most plentiful in the near future, as the need for replacing assistants is expected to grow. Other factors contributing to the rise in employment prospects will be a growing elderly population in need of dental care and a shift in the performance of routine duties from dentists to their assistants and hygienists.

Index: *American Dental Association, American Dental Assistants Association, American Medical Technologists, National Dental Association*

DENTAL LABORATORY TECHNICIAN

Description: Dental laboratory technicians make and repair dentures (artificial teeth), crowns, bridges, and other dental appliances according to dentists' prescriptions. They follow a specialized process which involves the use of synthetic and natural materials for models; small precision instruments for measuring and shaping; furnaces; grinding machines; and other specialized laboratory equipment. The technicians strive to produce "teeth" which are identical to the patient's own. There are five areas in which a dental laboratory technician may choose to specialize: *complete denture specialists* (manufacture teeth to fit in a complete upper or lower denture base), *crown and bridge technicians* (permanently restore adjacent teeth utilizing metal and porcelain), *dental ceramists* (create porcelain and acrylic restorations), *orthodontic technicians* (make orthodontic appliances), and *partial denture technicians* (for patients missing one or more teeth).

Most dental laboratory technicians work in commercial dental laboratories which tend to have few employees and are privately owned and operated. Other employment opportunities may be in larger laboratories, hospitals, dentist's offices and in self-employment. Technicians can expect to be at their workbench at least 40 hours a week, while the self-employed may put in more hours.

Education: On-the-job training provides the opportunity to master the skills necessary for a dental laboratory technician. It is not uncommon for the training to last up to four years due to the complexity of some procedures. Formal schooling is also an option, and in 1995, there were 37 accredited programs offered by community colleges and vocational technical institutes. Usually lasting two years, these programs award an associate degree and are followed by practical experience. Certification may be sought in one of the five specialty areas.

Salary, Future Outlook: Dental laboratory technicians can expect to earn more than the 1995 average of $23,723 a year. With more experience this amount may rise substantially; entry level workers should expect minimum wage.

According to 1996 statistics, there were 47,000 dental laboratory technicians in the workforce. Trainee positions are expected to be abundant over the next ten years although overall employment of technicians is likely to drop. Advances in preventive dental care will diminish the demand for tooth and teeth replacement, and computers may assume some of the workload once handled exclusively by technicians.

Index: *American Dental Association, National Association of Dental Laboratories, National Dental Association*

REGISTERED DENTAL HYGIENIST

Description: Registered dental hygienists (RHDs) are licensed professionals who provide a variety of oral health services. They scale and polish teeth; apply cavity-preventive agents, such as fluoride and sealant; expose, process, and interpret X-rays; monitor patients' medical and oral health; examine teeth and oral cavities; place temporary fillings and periodontal dressings; remove sutures, polish metal restorations, teach proper brushing and flossing techniques, and design and implement community or school oral health programs. In some states, registered dental hygienists administer local anesthetics, place and carve filling materials, and perform other periodontal procedures after acquiring additional education.

Hygienists commonly work in private dental offices although there are employment opportunities in public health, schools, clinics, and hospitals. An attractive feature of this career is its adaptability to any lifestyle- for example, working weekend or evening hours, if days are inconvenient. Working part-time in more than one office is not uncommon.

Education: Registered dental hygienists must graduate from an accredited dental hygiene program and pass a written and clinical examination to be licensed by the state in which they choose to practice. There are over 200 such programs in the United States, most of which award an associate's degree. Bachelor's or master's degrees are also offered, but are only necessary for those interested in education, research, or administration. Each program may have unique requirements for acceptance, but at least one year of college is recommended.

Salary, Future Outlook: The salary range for dental hygienists is wide, but those working full-time averaged $759 a week in 1995. Monetary compensation in this field is directly affected by location, education and experience.

Projections well into the next ten years suggest employment growth for registered dental hygienists. Advances in dentistry and improvements in oral hygiene translate into an increase in the percentage of elderly who will, without a need for dentures, require dental care. Also, hygienists will be assuming more of the duties that were once performed exclusively by dentists.

Index: *American Dental Association, American Dental Hygienists Association, National Dental Association*

Dietetic professionals are experts in an area which serves as a favorite pastime for many American — eating! *Dietitians*, *dietetic technicians and assistants*, and *nutritionists* educate the public about what we put into our bodies and how it affects our health.

In hospitals and nursing homes, these workers perform the crucial task of designing healthy personalized meals that adhere to any restrictions mandated by a patient's medical problems. Today, the public is more health conscious and more obsessed with physical appearances than in previous generations. Nutritionists can design and present educational programs for communities and individuals to teach them the importance of good nutrition and its beneficial effects on health, energy, appearance, and general attitudes toward life.

For people-oriented, motivated, and caring individuals interested in nutrition, a career in dietetics will provide them access to a health care field that is likely to grow well into the 21st century.

DIETITIAN AND NUTRITIONIST

Description: Registered dietitians (RDs) and Nutritionists are recognized as experts on food and nutrition; they promote and maintain health, prevent or treat illness, and aid rehabilitation through nutrition education and diet intervention. There are many specific types of dietitians including: *business dietitians* (employed by the food industry in sales, marketing, and public relations to ensure consumer satisfaction), *clinical dietitians* (deal with patients' nutritional concerns in hospitals and nursing homes; may specialize in diabetic, heart or kidney patients), *community dietitians* (counsel groups or individuals in public, government or home health agencies), *consultant dietitians* (work with facilities or individual clients), *educator dietitians* (teach physicians, nurses, and future dietitians the science of nutrition in schools and training programs), and *research dietitians* (conduct nutritional research for the government, food industry or pharmaceutical companies). *Nutritionist* is a general occupational title for health professionals concerned with food science and human nutrition. This includes *dietitians, home economists, food technologists, community nutritionists,* and *nutrition educators.*

The majority of dietitians and nutritionists are employed by hospitals and nursing homes. Federal and state governments also hire dietitians to work in public health, policy/administration, and research. Other dietitians may be employed by colleges and universities, school systems, diet and fitness centers, and home health agencies. Those that are self-employed are typically consultant dietitians who are hired by individual clients or large facilities. This field is conducive to the 40-hour work week, although opportunities do exist on a part-time basis and during non-traditional hours.

Education: To become a practicing dietitian, one must obtain a bachelor's degree in nutrition or dietetics, and acquire an adequate amount of experience in the field. A student may obtain a four-year degree that combines academic instruction with the necessary experience, or may first earn a bachelor's degree and then train in the field for one to two years. All programs must be approved and accredited by the American Dietetic Association. Upon completion of their training, dietitians may sit for a certification exam to earn the title RD. Advanced training increases qualifications for jobs in research and clinical facilities. A nutritionist may or may not have a degree in nutrition. The American Academy of Nutrition, founded in 1985, was the first accredited independent study program focusing solely on nutrition. The Academy offers an accredited program which awards the Associate of Science degree in Applied Nutrition, as well as continuing education credits for individuals in all fields and backgrounds.

Salary, Future Outlook: For dietitians, the more years of experience, the greater the earning potential. The median for all full-time dietitians in 1997 was $34,400. Registered dietitians with advanced training can also expect to earn an increased salary.

If the current trend of healthy eating and preventive lifestyle restructuring continues into the next century, the services of dietitians and nutritionists will be in great demand. However, as hospitals scale back their services and hire inexpensive employees to assume additional job responsibilities, dietitians may not find employment opportunities as easily. On the other hand, the increasing elderly population will require dietitian services for nursing home care and home health care. Overall, job growth is expected to be near the national average.

Index: *American Academy of Nutrition — College of Nutrition, The American Dietetic Association, Society for Nutrition Education*

DIETETIC TECHNICIAN AND DIETETIC ASSISTANT

Description: Dietetic technicians and dietetic assistants aid registered dietitians in nutrition care services and work in food service administration. A dietetic technician screens patients to identify nutrition problems and provides patient education and counseling to individuals or groups. They may oversee food service personnel and be responsible for monitoring food inventories and ordering supplies. Dietetic assistants also work directly under a dietitian, but usually assume more clerical food service duties.

Dietetic technicians and assistants can be found in all the sites where one finds a registered dietitian. These include hospitals, nursing homes, governmental departments, diet and fitness centers, and public health facilities. Technician and assistant positions are often more convenient for those seeking part-time employment and provide good work experience for students interested in a career in dietetics.

Education: Training for dietetic technicians is offered by community colleges and vocational-training schools. Generally, students enroll in a two year associate's degree program that has been approved by the American Dietetic Association. After fulfilling academic and practical work experience requirements, one may take the Registration Examination for Dietetic Technicians and, upon passing, become a Dietetic Technician, Registered (DTR). Dietetic assistants require no formal training and will learn appropriate skills on the job.

Salary, Future Outlook: A dietetic technician's salary will vary according to geographical location, experience and degree of responsibility. In 1997, registered dietitians earned close to $34,000 in entry level positions. Technicians working under these dietitians should expect to earn a salary less than that, but can advance with extra schooling. Because assistant positions require no specialized training, they earn a salary that approximates minimum wage.

The job outlook for registered dietitians in the dietetic field may be used as an indicator for technicians and assistants as well. As hospitals, nursing homes, and other facilities seek to save money, they may hire dietetic technicians and assistants to assume important duties.

Index: *The American Dietetic Association, American Health Care Association*

Percentage of Registered Dietitians Per Work Setting, 1997

Hospital/acute care 44%
Long term care 25%
Outpatient care 20%
Community/public health 20%
Private practice 11%
Other 10%

Source: American Dietetic Association Practice Audit

EMERGENCY MEDICINE

It takes a special person to be an emergency medical technician, someone who has the ability to think fast and stay calm in an emergency. EMTs respond to medical emergencies in the field and provide immediate care to the critically ill or injured. For those individuals choosing to enter emergency health care, there are three basic categories of employment: *EMT-B (Basic)*, *EMT-I (Intermediate)* and *EMT-P (Paramedic)*.

Operating in groups of two, these emergency workers are usually the first medical care providers on the scene of an accident. EMTs stabilize and monitor patients in specially equipped vehicles while en route to a medical facility, where they give a detailed account of the patient's status.

The irregular work hours and life-or-death decisions made by EMTs are understandably stressful, but may appeal to those who wish to embark upon a challenging career in health care.

EMERGENCY MEDICAL TECHNICIAN

Overall, there were 150,000 emergency medical technician (EMT) jobs in 1996. Twenty-five percent worked in hospitals, 30% worked for police, fire or rescue squads, and 40% held jobs with private ambulance services. It is not uncommon for EMTs in rural areas to be unpaid volunteers. Irregular and long working hours, often over 50 hours a week, are typical.

EMT-BASIC

Description: An EMT-Basic (EMT-B) has the least amount of training needed to qualify as an emergency medical technician. Along with other EMTs, an EMT-B performs basic life support skills such as: opening airways, restoring breathing, controlling blood loss, treating shock victims, immobilizing fractures, bandaging wounds, childbirth assistance, treating heart attack victims, and caring for poison and burn victims, etc. An EMT-B is accustomed to using such equipment as stretchers, backboards, oxygen devices and splints.

Education: Training for an EMT-B consists of 100-120 hours of classroom exercises and ten internship hours in a hospital emergency room. These training programs are often offered through hospitals, police and fire departments, and some colleges. Upon completing the program, a trainee must pass written and practical examinations at the state or national level to be awarded the title of Registered EMT-Basic.

Salary, Future Outlook: As seen in the salary chart derived from the *Journal of Emergency Medical Services*, the type of employer affects the salary of an EMT-B. In 1996, the average starting salary of an EMT-B was $25,051.

EMT-INTERMEDIATE

Description: An EMT-Intermediate (EMT-I) can perform the same tasks as an EMT-B and is also skilled in more advanced treatment, including the administration of intravenous (IV) fluids, and the use of defibrillators to restart a stopped heart.

Education: EMT-Is require additional training which includes 35-55 hours worth of instruction beyond that needed by an EMT-Basic. They learn more about patient assessment, esophageal airways, IV fluids, and anti-shock garments. Once registered as an EMT-B - and having met the classroom, clinical, and internship requirements – an EMT-B may choose to take the EMT-I examination to become registered.

Salary, Future Outlook: As it is not uncommon for an individual to progress directly from an EMT-B to an EMT-P, salary information for an EMT-I is not readily available.

EMT-PARAMEDIC

Description: EMT-Paramedics (EMT-P) undergo the most training of all EMTs and may administer the most advanced emergency care. Additional procedures include administering oral and IV drugs, electrocardiogram interpretation, performing endotracheal intubations, and using complex monitors and equipment. In rural areas, EMT-Ps may be allowed to treat patients on the scene in lieu of taking them to an emergency medical facility.

Education: As stated, the training of an EMT-P is the most comprehensive and requires an additional 750-2,000 hours of training beyond the requirements of an EMT-B. In 1993, there were 85 such programs in the United States. Qualification as a Registered EMT-P requires current status as an EMT-B, completion of the training program for EMT-Ps, ample field and clinical work, as well as passing the written and practical exams.

The extra training of the EMT-P usually translates to a salary which is higher than that of other EMTs. In 1996, the average starting salary was $30,407 for paramedics.

Salary, Future Outlook: Employment rates for all EMTs are expected to increase in the next ten years; the jobs with the highest salaries will be most competitive. An increase in the number of elderly, an increase in the EMTs' range of duties, and the extremely high turnover rate for this career are the biggest causes of this increase. Those choosing to advance beyond the EMT-P level may seek employment at an administrative level as a supervisor or director of emergency services. Others may opt for careers in fire and police departments, EMT instruction, or continue their education in the medical field.

Index: *Commission on Accreditation of Allied Health Education Programs, National Association of Emergency Medical Technicians*

EMT Annual Salary by Employer, 1996

	EMT-P	EMT-Basic
All employers	$30,407	$25,051
Fire departments	$32,483	$29,859
Hospital based	$28,373	$18,686
Private ambulance services	$23,995	$18,617

Source: Journal of Emergency Medical Services

Health care professionals in the area of information and communication are often overlooked when considering the key contributors to our nation's health. In reality, the work of these individuals is indispensable. They have produced a wealth of studies and reports detailing the recent advances and breakthroughs in science and medicine.

Biophotographers, medical illustrators, and *medical, science, and technical writers* produce visual and written materials on health topics, while *health sciences librarians* funnel this information into accessible collections and databases. *Health information managers* maintain and organize the host of patient charts, documents, and reports that accumulate in large patient care facilities and hospitals.

The accuracy of the work done by health information and communication professionals is crucial, as it ensures and fosters medical progress. As the expanding application of computers and the World Wide Web continue to revolutionize information and communication systems, these professionals will keep the health care field on the cusp.

Approximate Salary Ranges for Health Information Managers, 1997

Department Director	$30,000-$80,000
Assistant Department Director	$25,000-$65,000
Consultant	$25,000-$100,000
Clinical Coder	$22,000-$55,000

Source: American Health Information Management Agency

BIOPHOTOGRAPHER

Description: In order to photograph and document scientific information, biophotographers are specially trained in the areas of medicine, biology, chemistry, or other health subjects. Typically, their work is used in research reports, scientific publications, medical journals, or textbooks. In addition to being skilled in all technical aspects of photography, biophotographers must also be familiar with the biological sciences. A unique technique employed by biophotographers is photomicrography, which allows a microscopic object, such as a virus or bacteria, to appear in full detail to the unaided eye. A biophotographer may also document a surgical procedure, photograph an autopsy, or create a visual record of specimens. Biophotographers may choose to specialize in the areas of dental or ophthalmic photography.

Often, biophotographers are employed by major medical, dental, veterinary and health schools and organizations. Many zoological, wildlife, or agricultural societies may also utilize a biophotographer's skills. Pharmaceutical companies, publishing houses, and hospitals need biophotographers to aid in the depiction of microscopic and macroscopic events. Depending on the place of employment, a biophotographer's hours will vary. Although some are employed in jobs that have a standard 40-hour work week, others produce photographs as a part-time second job, or are self-employed and make their own hours.

Education: For most biophotography positions, on-the-job training will not suffice. Formal training programs are offered by colleges, vocational-technical schools, and trade schools are usually two to four years in length. If one chooses to obtain a college degree in photography, courses related to a specific scientific or medical field are also required. The Biological Photographic Association conducts a certification program which will register all successful individuals as a RBP (Registered Biologic Photographer).

Salary, Future Outlook: In 1996, the average annual salary for a full-time photographer was $30,600. Typically, a biophotographer who specializes in a field such as medicine or biology will earn more. In most cases, earnings will increase with additional education or a reputation established by working in the field for a significant number of years.

As the health industry experiences drastic advances in technology, and the field of medicine engages in continued scientific discovery, biophotographers will be called upon to document these developments and their outcomes. In the biophotography field itself, technical improvements will enhance the biophotographers' products and make their services more attractive. Because the field is small, new job openings will spawn fierce competition. Those biophotographers with the most advanced education or greatest career experience will have an advantage over new entrants to the field.

Index: *Biological Photographic Association, Health Science Communications Association*

HEALTH SCIENCES LIBRARIAN

Description: Health sciences librarians provide access to medical and health-related information for health professionals, medical researchers, students, and patients. Responsibilities include: locating specialized and up-to-date medical reference information via print and on-line sources; choosing and purchasing books and journals for health professionals; organizing health science books, journals and computerized databases for quick and easy usage; providing slides, films, and videotapes for medical and nursing education; teaching health care students and professionals how to use information resources; and library administrative tasks such as planning, budgeting, and personnel management.

Health sciences librarians are employed in hospitals, medical schools, federal agencies, pharmaceutical companies, and health information centers. Often, librarians will be employed on a part-time basis in small institutions, and on a full-time basis in larger medical school libraries. As a specialized librarian, a health sciences librarian will normally work a standard 35- to 40-hour week.

Education: For most health sciences librarian positions, a master's degree in library science (MLS) is mandatory. The American Library Association accredits over 50 schools with master's programs of one to two years in length. Typically, a bachelor's degree in a liberal arts subject is needed for admission to one of these programs; knowledge of a foreign language may be required as well. Those interested in health science librarianship may choose to seek a doctoral degree, professional degree, or other form of subject specialization in a medical, health, or science-related field.

Salary, Future Outlook: As with any career, the more experience, the greater the earning potential. For medical librarians with one year or less experience, the average salary was $25,900 in 1995. In that same year, the average income for all health sciences librarians was close to $40,800. Generally, those librarians with advanced degrees or extensive specialization will tend to earn the highest salary.

With the current outpouring of genetic research information, AIDS research findings, information on disease detection and transmission, and various other scientific test results, health sciences librarians are needed to handle the organization of this information. Librarians on the whole are likely to see a decreased job market over the next ten years, as computers may soon replace the librarian as quicker and more efficient information organizers. As long as medical publishing continues to be a growing industry, however, health sciences librarians will be needed to manage the wealth of materials that will be produced.

Index: *Health Sciences Communications Association, Medical Library Association*

MEDICAL ILLUSTRATOR

Description: Medical illustrators are artists who create graphics to meet the requirements of communication media for the biosciences. This work may be used in publications, film, television, exhibits, and three-dimensional models. Because of the variety of assignments in medical illustration, the artists must be accomplished in drawing, painting, and modeling techniques as well as experienced in the media and materials of commercial art. A medical illustrator may work as a member of a research team to provide illustrations and assist with the problem. Medical illustrators may also be responsible for preparing charts, graphs, and tables of statistical data. Some artists specialize in preparing artificial body parts such as noses, eyes, or ears to be used when patients require cosmetic or functional improvements. Still others prepare models for instructional purposes. They must have a strong foundation in anatomy and general medical knowledge to ensure the authenticity of their work.

Medical schools and research centers employ the majority of medical illustrators. Other employers include hospitals, clinics, medical publishers, pharmaceutical companies, and attorneys. Some medical illustrators may work on a freelance basis or may be employed by a medical publishing firm. Generally, medical illustrators will work a standard 40-hour week but self-employed artists may have non-traditional hours.

Education: A master's degree from an accredited institution is generally required for most positions in medical illustration. There are very few programs in the United States, with each program accepting fewer than 20 students a year. The normal length of these programs is two years. At the undergraduate level, courses in biology and art are equally important for admission to graduate schools. Within each training program, the student may specialize in a specific area of medical illustration such as surgery, veterinary illustration, or animation. The Association of Medical Illustrators offers continuing education programming to keep its members abreast of medical developments and illustrative techniques.

Salary, Future Outlook: Medical illustrators can usually expect to earn more than their graphic and visual artist counterparts in other fields. Full-time visual artists earned an average of $27,100 in 1996. However, with established experience, medical illustrators can earn up to three times this amount. The employer and area of specialization also factor into actual income.

Because training programs are limited and new graduates in the field of medical illustration are few, job opportunities are abundant. As advances in medical research are made, more illustrators will be needed to document research results. Lawyers will increasingly refer to forensic medical illustrators for assistance in courtroom demonstrations. In all areas where computerized graphic programs fail to rival the accuracy and efficiency of human artists, the skills of illustrators will be in demand.

Index: *Association of Medical Illustrators, Commission on Accreditation of Allied Health Education Programs, Health Sciences Communications Association*

HEALTH INFORMATION MANAGER

Description: The health information management professional collects, analyzes, and manages the information that steers the health care industry. In dealing with patient records, the health information manager must respect individual patient privacy yet contribute to quality care by organizing the medical data. These information specialists are skilled in the following areas: health care databases and database systems, medical classification systems, flow of clinical information, relationship of financial information to clinical data, uses and users of health care information, and medical legal issues and security systems.

There are three types of health information managers: *medical records administrators, medical records technicians,* and *certified coding specialists.* The medical records administrator (RRA), is a health service manager who directs activities in the medical records department of a health facility. He or she may establish departmental policy, objectives and procedures, coordinate with other managers, and oversee the other workers in their department. The medical record technician (ART) ensures that patient reports are complete and accurate for computer entry, and may confer with physicians to obtain missing information. The certified coding specialist (CCS) utilizes an established coding system to document procedures and diagnoses. Insurance companies make use of these codes to monitor patients' health expenses and bill them as needed.

Over half of all health information managers are employed by hospitals. Other facilities that require their services are nursing homes, HMOs, clinics, and physicians' offices. Insurance and accounting firms may also hire information managers to monitor the data that they receive from the health industry. Hospital facilities that are in service 24 hours a day are usually staffed with health records administrators and technicians at all times. On average, a full-time health information manager will work close to 40 hours a week.

Education: Positions in medical records administration are usually awarded to applicants with at least a bachelor's degree in health administration. A master's degree in administration was offered by 69 accredited programs in 1995 and may be necessary for employment in larger facilities. The American Health Information Management Association (AHIMA) conducts a certification exam and awards the credential of Registered Record Administrator (RRA). Medical records technicians generally have an associate's degree from a two-year community college or junior college program. In 1995, there were 134 technician programs and an Independent Study Program offered by AHIMA. After passing an exam, technicians receive the title Accredited Record Technician (ART). Certified coding specialists typically receive specific training but may not require a degree. AHIMA also conducts this certifying examination and awards all successful parties the title of Certified Coding Specialist (CCS).

Salary, Future Outlook: Medical records technicians and coding specialists earned an average annual salary of $31,200 in 1996. Additional education or years of experience result in a higher income for these workers.

Although the health information management field and the number of specialists it employs are expected to grow, there is likely to be a shift from employment in hospitals to MCOs, home health care agencies, and nursing homes. As hospitals scale back on spending and consolidate departments, they will be less likely to hire more administrators and technicians. As the elderly population increases and MCOs continue to grow, other health care facilities will require the services of these health information professionals.

Index: *American Health Care Association, American Health Information Management Association, Commission on Accreditation of Allied Health Education Programs, Health Sciences Communications Association*

MEDICAL, SCIENCE, TECHNICAL WRITER

Description: Medical, science, and technical writers are involved in a variety of activities, including presenting health information in an informative and interesting form for the public and making professional, scientific and technical information available to health specialists. They may write for newspapers, magazines, radio, or television. Technical writers deal with the same subject matter as do science writers, but while *technical writers* draw an audience of professionals in the field, *science writers* translate technical information into language that lay people can understand. *Medical writers and editors* are trained journalists who write or edit health-related books, articles, and brochures on a freelance basis or as part of a professional staff.

Medical, science and technical writers may be employed by print or electronic media while other such writers may be employed by pharmaceutical companies, universities and medical colleges, federal agencies, professional societies, or industrial research companies. Voluntary health agencies (VHAs) often focus their efforts on publicizing the results of medical research and will hire medical, science, and technical writers specifically for this. Typically, medical, science and technical writers operate on a 35-40 hour work week.

Education: Medical, science and technical writers must not only master journalistic and reporting skills, but also have a firm understanding of technical and scientific terminology. Often, these writers obtain a bachelor's degree in journalism or English from undergraduate institutions. Some employers may prefer a writer with a science degree, but generally will accept a liberal arts major who has completed science coursework. Institutions in the United States may offer specific courses in medical, science, or technical writing, but these courses are not always necessary for employment. Writers may pick up necessary writing skills simply by working in a medical or science laboratory, or functioning as a technical assistant. The education and training required for employment in these fields is very job-specific.

Salary, Future Outlook: Owing to the specialized nature of the services that medical, science and technical writers provide, they tend to earn more than the average writer. While writers and editors averaged $21,000 in 1996, technical writers averaged $44,000. This applies to medical and scientific writers, as well. Writers with journalism/ English degrees and a science degree, or those who have an advanced master's or doctoral degree will generally earn a salary at the upper end of the pay scale.

The future for medical, science and technical writers looks bright. Today, researchers and theorists are producing new studies, hypotheses, and findings more rapidly than ever before. Often, scientists engage in a race to get their results published, and depend on writers to accurately inform the rest of the scientific community and the public. As the public interest in medical and scientific advancement grows, all facets of the media will be looking for writers to satisfy this demand for information.

Index: *Health Sciences Communications Association, National Association of Science Writers, Inc.*

HEALTH SERVICES ADMINISTRATOR

The health care industry is undergoing a drastic change in organization and management. MCOs, in an effort to provide comprehensive health care at lower costs to patients, are replacing the independent fee-for-service practitioner. Hospitals are consolidating and downsizing in an attempt to cut costs, and doctors are beginning to encounter a new type of patient — one who is concerned with preventive health care and demands high quality at a lower cost.

At the center of this shift in health care are the health service administrators — professionals who head the health "business." Health services administrators, also known as health service generalists, include a top administrator or *chief executive officer (CEO)*, and *assistant administrators* who manage individual departments. *Long-term care administrators* are also included in the category of health service administrators, but they are specifically affiliated with nursing homes and assisted living facilities.

As the health care system continues to be remodeled and refined as a business, administrators will be needed to assure that the industry continues to offer high-quality care while preserving the bottom line.

HEALTH SERVICE ADMINISTRATOR

Description: The *chief executive officer* of a hospital or HMO serves as its primary administrator responsible for daily functioning and long-term development. Responsible for the business aspects of their institution, they focus on marketing, finances, human resources, and public relations. CEOs also coordinate their health programs with community groups and government agencies. *Assistant administrators* assist the CEO by managing most of the daily workings of the health organization. Usually, these administrators will specialize in a specific area of the organization's operation, such as clinical services, administrative services, or human resources. While assistant administrators may or may not be skilled in a health science, *clinical managers* are the administrative specialists who are trained medical professionals. *A long-term care administrator* may fulfill many of the same duties as other health care administrators, but often controls smaller facilities with individualized needs.

About half of all health service administrators are employed in hospitals, but that percentage is likely to decline. Increasingly, administrators are finding positions in nursing homes, MCOs, physician group practices, home health agencies and medical laboratories. Chief executive officers of large hospitals and MCOs may be called upon at any time to deal with business or administrative issues, and may have to travel extensively. Health service administrators can find positions in one of the many voluntary health agencies (VHAs) in this country as well. VHAs are health advocacy organizations which rely on committed administrators to conduct public policy programs and facilitate the sponsorship of medical research. VHA administrators may work beyond the typical 40-hour week and need to be available during odd hours.

Education: The type of education needed to qualify for health service administration positions will vary from job to job. Degrees in health administration are available at the bachelor's, master's, and doctoral levels from various colleges, universities, and health professional schools. For most positions beyond entry level, at least a master's degree is necessary. In 1995, there were 69 master's degree programs in health services administration, and admission was competitive. Some programs are designed for students wishing to specialize in the administration of a specific facility, while others offer a more generalized approach. A degree in public health, business administration, or one of the health sciences may be useful in and of itself and in seeking more advanced administrative positions. CEOs of large hospitals or other health facilities often have advanced degrees such as a PhD or even an MD. Nursing home administrators have stricter educational requirements and regulations. They must have at least a bachelor's degree, pass a licensing examination, and complete an "Administrator-in-Training" program offered by the state.

Salary, Future Outlook: The salary earned in administrative health care positions varies by facility size and level of responsibility. In 1997, administrators of small group practices and large group practices earned $56,000 and $77,000 respectively. In 1997, the majority of hospital CEOs earned more than $190,500, with some making well above that. Nursing home administrators earned an average of $49,500 in 1996, with assistant administrators earning close to $32,000.

As MCOs and long-term care facilities grow in number over the next ten years, the demand for health service administrators will increase. While hospitals used to be the primary employer of these workers, downsizing and smaller budgets will result in a reduced demand for new hospital administrators. Administrative jobs in all sectors of health care are likely to be very competitive and applicants with the most experience or extensive training will have an advantage in the pursuit of these positions. The number of new CEO positions will be low, but turnover at this high level will open opportunities for lower level administrators to move up.

Index: *American College of Health Care Administrators, American College of Healthcare Executives, Association of University Programs in Health Administration*

Today's medical field is much more specialized than it was just a few generations ago. The doctors who made house calls to treat patients of all ages and symptoms of all types have disappeared. Today, patients visit HMO clinics or choose from a select group of physicians who are included under their health insurance plan.

Many of these changes resulted from the revolutionary medical advances that have expanded the health care field. In addition to seeing a general *allopathic physician* (better known as a Medical Doctor, or MD), patients have the option of visiting an *osteopathic physician, chiropractor, physician assistant* or a physician specialist from one of over 20 specialty fields.

The remodeling of health care into a profit-conscious business has probably been more influential than all of the technological advances the medical industry has experienced. Like any successful business, the health care industry must offer the public a high-quality product at a reasonable cost. Assistant personnel like *chiropractic technicians and assistants, medical assistants, medical secretaries, physician assistants,* and *podiatric medical assistants* will see increased job opportunities as a result of this cost maintenance trend.

CHIROPRACTOR

Description: Also known as Doctors of Chiropractic (DC), chiropractors believe that health problems are linked directly to problems of the muscular, nervous and skeletal systems. By using manipulation concentrated on the spinal column and vertebrae, chiropractors try to alleviate any stresses that may be affecting the nervous system. Normal body function and resistance to disease are in this way restored. The aim of chiropractic medicine is holistic health, and chiropractors often advise patients on ways to improve their lifestyle and habits. Eschewing surgery, medication, or other invasive means, chiropractors instead focus on nutrition, water, light or massage therapies, exercise, and spinal adjustment. In a manner similar to physicians in other fields, Doctors of Chiropractic do ask for patient histories, perform patient examinations, and order laboratory tests.

The majority of chiropractors, close to 70%, choose to work in a solo practice, while group practice, research positions, teaching jobs, and employment in hospitals or HMOs are in the minority. The typical Doctor of Chiropractic will work over 40 hours a week; a solo practitioner often works longer hours and must also manage the administrative duties of running a business. Smaller communities, close to a school of chiropractic, are the choice locations for most practicing doctors.

Education: Admission requirements to schools of chiropractic vary widely, and individual states have their own licensing prerequisites. There are 17 chiropractic colleges in the United States, and all but two are accredited by the Council on Chiropractic Education. Most require two years of undergraduate study, while in some cases a bachelor's degree is needed for admission consideration. Chiropractic students undergo four years of training, and upon graduation from an accredited school will take a licensing examination at the national or state level.

Salary, Future Outlook: Chiropractors earned a median salary of $80,000 in 1995. As in any career, new entrants into the field made a lower wage, while some prosperous chiropractors earned over $170,000. Other factors affecting income may be location, type of practice, and size of clientele.

As more and more people learn about chiropractic medicine, the demand for chiropractors is likely to increase over the next ten years. In 1996, there were 44,000 chiropractic physicians in the United States, a number which will undoubtedly rise as more health insurance programs cover chiropractic expenses.

Index: *American Chiropractic Association, Council on Chiropractic Education*

CHIROPRACTIC TECHNICIAN/ASSISTANT

Description: A chiropractic assistant performs duties that aid the Doctor of Chiropractic in the practice of patient care. They have been educated in the history and philosophy of chiropractic medicine, and are also familiar with anatomical terms, technical procedures, and the administrative skills required to run a chiropractic practice successfully. Assistants are under director supervision of the chiropractor.

Education: At this time, neither an accredited training program nor licensing board exists for chiropractic assistants. In the near future it is likely that chiropractic assisting will become a licensed health care profession.

Salary, Future Outlook: Their demand is likely to increase as chiropractic practices expand and physicians relinquish some of their basic duties to other employees.

For more information, see **medical assistant**, which is a more general category.

Index: *American Chiropractic Association*

MEDICAL ASSISTANT

Description: Medical assistants help doctors by performing a variety of clinical and administrative duties. The scope of their duties generally depends on the size of the practice in which they are employed, with those in larger practices tending to be more specialized. Clerical or administrative duties may involve telephone monitoring, patient record organization, appointment scheduling, billing, and bookkeeping. Individual states have their own regulations as to which clinical duties a medical assistant may perform. Some common clinical assignments may be: taking vital signs, performing basic laboratory tests, disposing of or sterilizing laboratory supplies, drawing blood, or preparing patients for the physician. Generally, medical assistants can be employed in the office of physicians, podiatrists, chiropractors, and optometrists. Those who limit their scope exclusively to podiatry or chiropractic medicine for example, will assume duties related specifically to that type of medicine.

Education: A medical assistant may choose to work the standard 40-hour work week or opt for a more individualized or non-traditional schedule. Most medical assistants are employed in a physician's office, while the rest are distributed evenly among chiropractic, optometric, and podiatric practices. Assistants may also be needed to fill vacancies in other facilities, such as hospitals and nursing homes.

No formal training is needed to qualify for a job as a medical assistant. Usually, a high school diploma is sufficient, and training takes place on the job. For those who opt for formal training, programs are offered at vocational and technical schools, community or junior colleges, and at universities. One-year programs award a certificate or diploma while two-year programs usually award an associate's degree in medical assisting. The Commission of Accreditation of Allied Health Education Programs (CAAHEP) accredits around 221 assisting programs while the Accrediting Bureau of Health Education Schools (ABHES) offers 162 accredited training programs. Licensing is not required, but certification is offered by some organizations. For example, the American Association of Medical Assistants offers the Certified Medical Assistant credential.

Salary, Future Outlook: Medical assistants on the job for less than two years earned between $8.07 and $10.90 an hour in 1997. With more experience, earnings were reported in that same year of up to $13.46 an hour. Income is likely to vary by geographical location and previous experience.

In 1996, there were approximately 225,000 medical assistants employed in health care offices. In the next ten years, the demand for medical assistants will increase as the market for health services expands. With the changing face of health care, assistants will be invaluable to the large practices and outpatient facilities that are likely to dominate.

Index: *American Association of Medical Assistants, American Medical Technologists, Commission on Accreditation of Allied Health Education Programs*

MEDICAL SECRETARY

Description: A medical secretary performs all of the duties of a typical secretary, but does so in the specialized setting of a medical office. Like other secretaries, medical secretaries may process correspondence, transcribe dictation, prepare reports, or organize meetings for their employers. In addition, they may have direct patient interaction, and may communicate with hospitals and medical supply contacts.

Medical secretaries are usually employed in physicians' offices, but may also work in hospitals or other health care facilities. Most secretaries are full-time employees, although part-time and off-hour schedules are manageable.

Education: Anyone with basic office skills is eligible to be hired as a medical secretary and can be trained on the job. Extra training or advanced skills, however, make an applicant more attractive to an employer. Vocational-technical schools and community colleges often offer secretarial training courses, although those seeking a job as a medical secretary should enroll in a specialized training program. Familiarity with anatomy, technical procedures and laboratory techniques is useful, as is knowledge of health insurance and the computer programs typically used in physicians' offices.

Salary, Future Outlook: The average annual salary range of all secretaries in 1995 was from $19,700 to $40,600, depending on location, experience, and office setting.

Of the more than three million secretaries who were employed in 1996, 239,000 were medical secretaries. Although secretaries as a whole will likely experience a drop in employment, expansion in the health care industry will increase the demand for medical secretaries.

Index: *American Association of Medical Transcriptionists, National Association of Medical Staff Services*

M.D. Distribution by Specialty, 1995

PRIMARY CARE	
General internal medicine:	16.0%
General and family medicine	10.5%
General pediatrics:	7.0%

MEDICAL SPECIALTIES		OTHER SPECIALTIES	
Allergy	0.5%	Anesthesiology	4.6%
Cardiovascular disease	2.6%	Emergency medicine	2.7%
Dermatology	1.2%	General preventive medicine	0.2%
Obstetrics and gynecology	5.2%	Neurology	1.6%
		Nuclear medicine	0.2%
		Pathology	2.5%
SURGICAL SPECIALTIES		Physical medicine and rehabilitation	0.8%
Colon and rectal surgery	0.1%	Psychiatry	5.3%
General surgery	5.2%	Radiology	1.1%
Neurological surgery	0.7%	Others	8.3%
Ophthalmology	2.4%	Unspecified/unknown/inactive	14.4%
Orthopedic surgery	3.1%		
Otalaryngology	1.3%		
Plastic surgery	0.8%		
Thoracic surgery	0.3%		
Urological surgery	1.4%		

Source: American Medical Association, in Occupational Outlook Handbook (Bureau of Labor Statistics)

PHYSICIAN

Description: Physicians diagnose, treat, and work to prevent human illness, disease, or injury. They perform many functions, including but not limited to: patient examinations, analysis of patient histories, and interpretation of ordered diagnostic tests. Physicians stress preventive care and often counsel their patients on better health care practices. Physicians use accepted methods of medical treatment, including pharmaceutical agents and surgical procedures. There are two types of physicians: **allopathic physicians**, better known as the **MD (Medical Doctor)**, and **osteopathic physicians**, better known as the **DO (Doctor of Osteopathic Medicine)**. Although both MDs and DOs are physicians who may specialize, perform surgery, and prescribe medication, they differ in their health care philosophy and attend separate training schools. The specialties of both groups of physicians are identical and include: *allergy and immunology* (immune system specialist), *anesthesiology* (giving anesthetics for surgical procedures), *colon and rectal surgery* (regional surgery), *dermatology* (skin diseases), *emergency medicine* (treatment of emergency illnesses), *family practice* (comprehensive health care of the patient within the family unit), *internal medicine* (non-surgical disease), *neurological surgery* (brain and nervous system surgery), *neurology* (neural specialist), *nuclear medicine* (radioactivity used in disease diagnosis), *obstetrics and gynecology* (female reproductive health and childbirth), *ophthalmology* (eye specialist), *orthopedic surgery* (muscle and bones), *otolaryngology* (ear, nose and throat), *pathology* (analysis of disease and laboratory medicine), *pediatrics* (children), *physical medicine and rehabilitation* (rehabilitation of people who have suffered from a stroke, heart attack, or similar conditions), *plastic surgery* (corrective and cosmetic surgery), *preventive medicine* (disease prevention), *psychiatry* (mental health specialist), *radiology* (X-rays), *Surgery* (invasive treatment and procedures), *thoracic surgery* (regional surgery), and *urology* (male reproductive and unisex urinary tract health). While around 30% of MDs are primary care practitioners, the majority of DOs opt for primary care over specialization.

Salary, Future Outlook: Physicians typically seek employment in office-based practices, although employment by hospitals or the federal government is not uncommon. Sixty-hour work weeks are the norm for physicians and work loads are often reduced as they approach retirement. While MDs often choose to practice in urban areas, DOs are more likely to service smaller, rural populations, usually in states which contain an osteopathic medical school.

There were 560,000 working physicians (MDs and DOs) in 1996. The job outlook for the next decade is excellent due to changes in the health industry, and growth in the elderly population. Expect an increased demand for primary care physicians and a decreased need for specialists. Solo practitioners are also expected to be outnumbered by physicians employed in group practice, clinics and HMOs.

Index: *American Academy of Family Physicians, American Academy of Pediatrics, American College of Surgeons, American Psychiatric Association, Association of American Indian Physicians, Association of American Medical Colleges, American Association of Colleges of Osteopathic Medicine, American Osteopathic Association*

ALLOPATHIC PHYSICIAN

Education: Students seeking an MD degree usually obtain a bachelor's degree and must submit Medical College Admission Test (MCAT) scores along with transcripts and personal recommendations from undergraduate institutions. Competition is fierce for admission to the 125 allopathic medical schools in the United States, where a four-year curriculum is followed by a three- to eight-year residency, depending upon the doctor's area of specialization. MDs are licensed by the state after passing an examination, while the American Board of Medical Specialists (ABMS) administers an examination for board certification in a specialty area. A master's degree or a PhD may be needed to do research or teach.

Salary, Future Outlook: Allopathic physicians (MDs) characteristically have a salary that is much higher than the average national salary. While income varies by specialty, the median income for all MDs was $160,000 in 1995. Earnings depend on type of practice, location, hours worked, and many other factors. First-year medical residents earned $32,789 in 1996-97. For the first few years of practice, accumulated student loans from medical school and even undergraduate school may offset the higher income.

OSTEOPATHIC PHYSICIAN

Description: The philosophy of osteopathy differs from allopathic medicine. Osteopathic physicians (DOs) believe that musculoskeletal manipulation is the key to patient diagnosis and treatment. DOs relate the supportive structures of the body, such as bones, muscles, ligaments, and nerves, to body function.

Education: There are 17 osteopathic medical schools in the United States, and the prerequisites for acceptance are the same as those of allopathic medical schools. Students should also demonstrate an understanding of the osteopathic philosophy and be familiar with its principles and beliefs. After the four years of medical school and an examination offered by the National Board of Osteopathic Medical Examiners, DOs take a year-long rotating internship and may then enter a specialty program. The salary of a DO is comparable to that of an MD.

Number of People Receiving Care in HMOs

Year	Number
1986	25.7 million
1987	29.3 million
1988	32.7 million
1989	34.7 million
1990	36.5 million
1991	38.6 million
1992	41.4 million
1993	45.2 million
1994	51.1 million
1995	58.2 million estimated

Sources: Group Health Association of America National Directory of HMOs Database, American Association of Health Plans sample survey of HMOs and PPOs

OPHTHALMOLOGIST

Description: Ophthalmologists are licensed primary care physicians trained to practice a mixture of medicine and surgery. They cover all aspects of eye care, ranging from lens prescription to delicate surgical procedures. Ophthalmologists treat patients of all ages with vision-threatening diseases and disorders. They perform about half of the nation's refractions and eye examinations, with optometrists performing the other half. Ophthalmologists may choose to subspecialize in the areas of external eye disease, glaucoma, neuro-ophthalmology (pathology of the optic nerve or visual pathways), ophthalmic pathology, ophthalmic plastic surgery, pediatric ophthalmology, or vitreoretinal (inner eye) disease.

Ophthalmologists practice in a variety of work environments. Most ophthalmologists spend a large part of the working week in the office performing standard medical ophthalmologic treatments, and spend the remaining time in the hospital operating room performing surgical procedures.

Education: An ophthalmologist receives a minimum of 12 years of higher education. A candidate for ophthalmology will need four years of college, four years of medical school, one or more years of general clinical training, and three or more years in a hospital-based eye residency program. For subspecialties, a fellowship of one or more years is necessary.

Salary, Future Outlook: Salaries for ophthalmologists vary by specialization. General practitioners of ophthalmology will ordinarily earn between $100,000 to $125,000 a year. Specialization in areas such as vitreoretinal disease may yield a salary of $150,000 to $250,000 a year. According to a study in *Medical Economics* (September 7, 1998), the median salary for all ophthalmologists (general practitioners and specialists combined) was $193,510 in 1997.

There are approximately 17,500 full-time ophthalmologists practicing in the United States, up from 14,000 in 1992. The need for ophthalmologists may increase in the coming years as the population ages and as more individuals acquire age-related eye disorders.

Index: *American Academy of Ophthalmology*

PHYSICIAN ASSISTANT

Description: Physician assistants (PAs) work under a physician's supervision and perform many patient care tasks which were traditionally conducted by doctors. PAs do not have the same responsibilities as medical assistants, because the two careers each have their own distinct set of duties. Physician assistants perform complete physical examinations, diagnose illness, give treatments, order and review laboratory tests and X-rays, and counsel patients on their health problems. Although most PAs are allowed to prescribe medication, the state laws governing this practice may vary. PAs are always directly supervised by a physician; the extent of supervision depends upon the work setting. The majority of physician assistants choose to work in primary care, while the rest specialize in such areas as surgery (surgeon's assistant), emergency medicine, or pediatrics.

Because physician assistants work so closely with physicians, their work schedules may also be hectic and variable. Certain work settings, clinics especially, can usually guarantee a 40-hour work week. Physicians' offices employ the largest number of PAs, followed by health clinics, HMOs, federal government agencies, hospitals, nursing homes and correctional facilities. It is common for physician assistants to work in areas where physicians may be in short supply.

Education: Employment as a physician assistant requires training at an accredited PA program. There are currently over 70 such programs in the United States, typically affiliated with medical schools or schools of allied health. Applicants to a physician assistant program have a background in patient care and often have received a bachelor's or master's degree. After two years of study and training, graduates earn either a baccalaureate degree, associate's degree, master's degree, or a certificate of completion, depending on the program. Forty-nine states require a certifying exam for employment as a Physician Assistant-Certified (PA-C). To maintain this status, state regulations specify 100 hours of continuing medical education every two years and a rectification exam every six years. Additional education is often needed for specialization.

Salary, Future Outlook: In 1996, PAs working 40-hour weeks reported median earnings between $49,100 and $60,000. While first-year graduates tend to earn less money for their services, increases are likely with experience. Other variables in salary may be specialization, location, and work setting.

In 1996, there were 64,000 physician assistants employed in the United States and analysts predict this to be one of the fastest growing fields of the next decade. As the health industry seeks to cut health care costs, PAs will be asked to perform the duties of a physician at a significantly lower cost. The growth of managed care and Medicare recognition of PA services should increase the need for physician assistants.

Index: *American Academy of Physician Assistants, Commission on Accreditation of Allied Health Education Programs*

Distribution of Physician Assistants by Specialty, 1995

Family/general practice — 38.4%
General internal medicine — 8.9%
Surgery — 18.8%
Emergency medicine — 9.8%
Obstetrics/gynecology — 2.7%
General pediatrics — 2.7%
Internal medicine subspecialties — 6.2%

Source: American Academy of Physician Assistants, "1997 Annual Member Census."

PODIATRIST

Description: Podiatrists, also known as doctors of podiatric medicine (DPMs), prevent, diagnose, and treat disorders

of the foot and leg. They employ medical, surgical, mechanical, or physical means to treat deformities and growths of the foot, design casts and orthotics to treat injuries, and improve posture and walking style. Podiatrists also counsel and advise patients on preventive health care, and refer patients to other medical doctors if serious symptoms are present. Often, podiatrists are the first health care providers to recognize symptoms of heart disease, diabetes, or arthritis. In addition to general practice, DPMs may choose to be certified in the specialty areas of orthopedics, surgery, or public health. Some popular subspecialties are in sports medicine, geriatrics, pediatrics, or diabetic foot care.

The typical podiatrist has a home-based private independent practice. Partnerships and expanded practices appear to be gaining popularity, however. The majority of practices exist in states which also have a college of podiatric medicine. Other employment opportunities exist in hospitals, nursing homes, HMOs, and federal government agencies. The number of hours worked by a podiatrist varies by work setting; self-employed doctors often have weekend or evening hours to best accommodate their patients, while other settings are more conducive to 40-hour work weeks.

Education: There are currently seven colleges of podiatric medicine in the United States. Admission generally requires

a bachelor's degree and competitive scores on the Medical College Admissions Test (MCAT). After completing the four-year curriculum, graduates are awarded the doctor of podiatric medicine (DPM) degree. Hospital residencies range from one to three years, depending on the specialization. All states have their own licensing requirements, but it is standard to require graduation from an accredited school and a passing grade on the National Boards. Specialty boards grant certification to qualified individuals.

Salary, Future Outlook: In 1996, the median net income of podiatrists was $91,400 and a six-digit salary was common. Factors affecting deviation from the median value are location of practice, years of experience and number of patients.

Due to the small number of training colleges, there were only 11,000 working podiatrists in 1996. Future growth in the podiatric field is likely to be near the national average. Podiatrists will be needed to handle the growing number of elderly in the next ten years, but the small size of the occupation limits job opportunities. Often podiatrists work right up to retirement, and areas which are already well-supplied with DPMs are not likely to make room for new graduates.

Index: *American Colleges of Podiatric Medicine Application Service, American Podiatric Medical Association*

Society today places a much larger emphasis on mental health and social well-being than did previous generations. Career professionals specializing in mental and social health not only help individuals with severe emotional disabilities and psychological disorders, but also help clients resolve family conflicts, counsel victims of substance abuse, and work with the aged and disabled.

One group that will make greater use of *human services workers* and *social workers* in the near future is the elderly. These professionals will be called upon to assist the growing number of elderly in adjusting to increased physical limitations, while working to ensure that they have a satisfactory quality of life. This will be particularly important in dealing with elderly individuals who live alone and in some degree of isolation. While *genetic counselors* work with families that are disrupted by an inherited medical condition, *psychologists* similarly help clients of all ages to resolve stressful personal and familial issues. *Psychiatric mental health technicians* provide the bulk of daily care to those individuals with more serious mental handicaps and will increasingly be sought by private health institutions.

Fortunately, eliciting the help of a mental or social health professional does not necessarily carry with it the stigma of years past. Job opportunities for workers in this field will be plentiful as more people take advantage of the services these professionals provide.

GENETIC COUNSELOR

Description: Genetic counselors provide information and support to families who have members with birth defects or genetic disorders, and to families who may be at risk for a variety of inherited conditions. They investigate the problem present in the family, interpret information about the disorder, analyze inheritance patterns and risks of recurrence, and review available options with the family. Counselors may choose to focus on one aspect of genetics such as pediatric genetics, cancer genetics, neurogenetics, or prenatal treatment. Genetic counselors use their counseling skills, combined with a background in medical genetics, to assist families through emotional times.

Genetic counselors can use their skills in private practice, commercial research laboratories, public health clinics, MCOs, or federal agencies. Most, however, are employed by hospitals or university medical centers, where they are concentrated in pediatric and obstetric departments. Full-time, 40-hour business weeks are standard for genetic counselors, although some hospitals may request that they be on call for emergency situations.

Education: Those interested can obtain their master's degree in genetic counseling from one of the 23 training programs throughout the country. Graduate course work includes medical genetics, counseling topics, and hands-on experience in the field. An undergraduate degree in a biological science, psychology, public health, or other related field is usually necessary for admission into one of these training programs. The American Board of Genetic Counseling conducts the certification examination for those who have their graduate degree in genetic counseling and have an acceptable amount of work experience.

Salary, Future Outlook: The genetic counselor's salary will vary by geographical location, work setting and years of experience. New graduates should expect to earn an entry level salary of approximately $28,000. With experience, a genetic counselor can earn up to $53,000 a year.

Currently, there are close to 1,500 practicing genetic counselors in the United States. The small number of training programs and the small size of each graduating class ensures that the demand for genetic counselors should be great in the near future. As advances are made in genetic testing, prenatal screening, and reproductive technologies, genetic counselors will be essential well into the next century.

Index: *American Board of Genetic Counseling, National Society of Genetic Counselors*

Percentage of Genetic Counselors Per Work Setting, 1996

Setting	Percentage
University medical centers:	45%
Private hospital setting:	27%
HMO or other managed care setting:	5%
Physician or own private practice:	5%
Diagnostic laboratory setting:	5%
State or federal office:	4%

Percentage of Genetic Counselors Per Career Focus, 1996

Focus	Percentage
Prenatal setting:	52%
Pediatric genetics:	18%
Cancer genetics:	8%
Neurogenetics:	4%
Others:	12%

Source: National Society of Genetic Counselors, Inc. 1996 Professional Issues Survey of Full Membership

HUMAN SERVICES WORKER

Description: The title human services worker encompasses a broad range of careers in social work, mental health, and rehabilitation, among others. Some job titles that fall under this heading are *social service assistant, alcohol or drug abuse counselor, child care worker, gerontology aide, community support worker, life skills counselor, case management aide,* and *social work assistant.* Depending upon the job title and setting, workers responsibilities will vary. Generally, human services workers provide emotional support, give their clients information about services such as food stamps and Medicaid, provide transportation, counsel clients on lifestyle and coping habits, coordinate group and community activities, and keep an accurate record of client progress. Some human services workers supplement nursing duties, deal directly with psychological issues, or coordinate the activities of a rehabilitation program, counseling center, or nursing home.

Just as the job description of a human services worker varies, so does the work environment. Group homes, hospitals, clinics, and shelters all require the skills of these individuals. Government agencies, public welfare agencies, and private human service agencies employ human service workers as planners, coordinators, project managers, and field workers. Usually, human services workers will work full 40-hour weeks and business hours are more suited to some careers, while in-home or hospital workers may have evening, late night, or weekend shifts. These jobs often have high stress levels, but are also rewarding to those who enjoy helping others.

Education: Although a college degree is not necessary for human service work, it will make a job applicant more attractive to employers. High school graduates will be trained on the job, but their duties may be limited to direct care services. A certificate or an associate's, bachelor's, or higher degree qualifies the holder for positions in management or worker supervision, as well as for direct contact with clients. Community colleges, vocational-technical institutes, and other training sites offer certificates and associate's degrees, while there are close to 400 bachelor's degree programs. Those seeking administrative positions usually need a master's degree. Human services programs offer the most comprehensive training, although employers will generally still hire those with college degrees in social work, psychology, or behavioral science.

Salary, Future Outlook: Earnings for human services workers in 1997 ranged from a starting salary of $15,000-$24,000 to an experienced worker's salary of $20,000-$30,000. Education, years in the field, and the employer all will affect earnings.

In 1996, human services workers occupied 178,000 jobs in the United States. As the turnover rate for these professions remains high and the elderly population grows, the employment outlook for will remain excellent. Counseling and support services will always be in demand, and state and local governments are likely to continue to employ human services workers over the more expensive social worker and mental health professional. This occupation is likely to be one of the fastest growing for the next ten years.

Index: *National Organization for Human Service Education*

PSYCHIATRIC MENTAL HEALTH TECHNICIAN

Description: Psychiatric mental health technicians, also known as psychiatric aides, work with people with emotional or mental illness or mental retardation under the supervision of doctors, nurses, and other medical personnel. In some cases, they observe, interview, and counsel patients, and participate in their daily recreation, work, and treatment programs. They also perform simple nursing tasks, such as taking temperatures and giving out medications. Additionally, psychiatric mental health technicians may assist patients in dealing with problems occurring within the family, work, and community environments. Most important, they provide companionship and assistance to individuals who are isolated from the outside world.

Psychiatric mental health technicians are usually employed in hospital psychiatric wards, community mental health centers, state and county mental institutions, and private facilities. Some facilities may have aides on duty around the clock, or may simply need them during normal business hours. Full-time and part-time work schedules are possible within this field.

Education: Some psychiatric facilities may hire mental health technicians with no experience or training. Through on-the-job training, these aides learn their designated duties under close supervision. Some states, however, have mandatory training regulations that apply to all mental health employees. Training programs may be offered in vocational-technical schools, community colleges, or through mental health facilities. Good inter-personal skills and a willingness to help others are important traits for a successful mental health technician.

Salary, Future Outlook: In 1996, psychiatric mental health technicians earned approximately $292 per week. On a yearly basis, this translates to roughly $15,000. Factors such as years of experience, location, and work setting raise or lower salaries from the national average.

There were 103,000 psychiatric aide jobs in 1996, and one can expect average future growth in this profession. This growth will occur largely within private and community mental health facilities. An increase in the elderly population and a new generation of Americans who are less prejudiced toward those seeking mental help, are two reasons why psychiatric mental health technicians will still be in demand over the next ten years.

Index: *American Psychiatric Association*

PSYCHOLOGIST

Description: Psychologists are licensed mental health professionals trained to assess, diagnose, and treat mental disorders by using individual, child, family, and group therapies. There are many different types of psychologists who specialize in subjects linked to the health field. *Clinical psychologists* comprise the largest group of psychologists and may work with physicians in counseling emotionally disturbed individuals, medical and surgical patients, and chronically ill patients. *Health psychologists* work with patients trying to adopt healthy lifestyle behaviors and achieve personal health goals. *Geropsychologists* specialize in problems of the elderly, such as adapting to lifestyle limitations, keeping a healthy attitude about the future, and remaining active. *Counseling psychologists* advise clients on how to cope with everyday issues and help to resolve personal problems. Some other types of psychologists fall under the sub-specialties of *developmental, experimental, industrial-organizational, school, social, abnormal, neuro-, rehabilitation, educational,* and *sports psychology*.

Psychologists practice in varied settings, depending upon their specialty. Private practice psychologists have their own offices with hours tailored to meet patients' needs. Those employed by hospitals, nursing homes, and other medical facilities may need to cover late-night and weekend shifts. Other psychologists who work as faculty at colleges and universities, in government positions, or engage in research are likely to keep regular business hours. Psychologists may often work in more than one setting and divide their time accordingly.

Education: Training requirements depend on the psychology subspecialty. A bachelor's degree in psychology will qualify a person for assistant positions in research and administration but advancement will be severely limited. Psychologists with a master's degree may work as assistants, organizational or industrial psychologists, or school psychologists and counselors. A PhD degree is required for some clinical or counseling psychology positions and for most research and teaching positions. There are currently over 600 master's programs (two years) and PhD programs (five to seven years) offered at colleges and universities around the country. Upon completing schooling, a PhD student must complete a dissertation. A similar, but less common degree, the PsyD (Doctor of Psychology), is sought by those interested in clinical work and does not require a dissertation. States vary as to their licensing laws for psychologists. Certification is awarded by the American Board of Professional Psychology to those students with their doctorate, five years of experience, and completion of the certification examination.

Salary, Future Outlook: Psychologists' earnings vary by subspecialty and educational level. In 1995, psychologists with a master's degree earned an average of $43,000 in clinical psychology, $38,000 in counseling psychology, $41,500 in research, and even more for school psychology and industrial-organizational psychology. Those with a doctoral degree earned on average $55,000 in counseling psychology, $54,500 in research positions, $51,000 in clinical psychology, and up to $59,000 in school psychology. With more years of experience, salaries are likely to be higher.

In the year 2000 and beyond, the demand for psychologists should be great but the competition also will be fierce. Doctoral and master's level psychologists will be the most sought-after by employers and a bachelor's degree will not always guarantee a job in the field. MCOs, nursing homes, and drug abuse programs will need to use more psychologists as they expand. In 1994, 30% of all psychologists were employed in the health services settings of hospitals, clinics and other facilities. As the health care industry grows, more psychologists will be needed to perform health-related services.

Index: *American Psychological Association*

SOCIAL WORKER

Description: Social workers work with individuals, groups, and communities. In a medical setting, they help patients and their families deal with problems related to physical, mental, or emotional illness and disability. Working in the community, social workers assist residents in finding employment or housing and help initiate community projects. A social worker may provide personal counseling for individuals and families, or direct the client to appropriate information sources. There are many fields in which to specialize as a social worker, including: *child welfare and family services, child or adult protective services, mental health, health care, school social work, criminal justice, occupational social work, gerontology*, and *policy/planning*.

A social worker typically works a 40-hour week, with some of those hours on the weekend or during evening hours when clients have free time. Because the title of social worker encompasses so many duties, work settings will vary from person to person. In health care, social workers are predominantly employed in hospitals, clinics, mental health facilities, nursing homes, community and public health centers, federal agencies, and patient homes. They will often work alongside other health care providers such as physicians, nurses, and mental health professionals.

Education: An individual may qualify as a social worker at a number of educational levels. A bachelor's degree in social work (BSW) can be obtained from nearly 390 programs in the United States. These social workers must perform at least 400 hours of field service to be certified. A master's degree in social work (MSW) is offered by just over 100 colleges and universities, requires 900 hours of field work and takes two years to earn. The MSW degree is appropriate for those interested in health and mental health social work, or for any supervisory or administrative position. The Doctor of Social Work degree (DSW), with approximately 60 programs across the United States, is required for college and university teaching positions and any formal research in social work. Licensing and certification laws regarding social workers vary from state to state. The National Association of Social Workers awards many credential designations including ACSW (Academy of Certified Social Workers), ACBSW (Academy of Certified Baccalaureate Social Workers), and QCSW (Qualified Clinical Social Worker).

Salary, Future Outlook: In 1997, social workers with a master's degree earned on average $35,000 while those with a bachelor's degree earned a median of $25,000. A hospital social worker averaged $35,000 in 1997. Income determining factors included number of years of experience, education, and geographical location.

In 1996, there were close to 585,000 social workers employed in the United States and that number is expected to grow. For social workers in the health care field, job outlook will be great over the next ten years. The current trend in health care toward quicker hospital discharge and outpatient-based care will mean that more social workers will be called upon to visit patients in the home. The mentally ill and disabled will continue to require social work services, and the growing elderly population will provide a giant client base for all social workers.

Index: *American Health Care Association, National Association of Social Workers*

Nursing is projected to be one of the fastest growing health care fields through the year 2000 and beyond. However, the title "nurse" is much too general to define this group of professionals. Instead, there are *homemaker-home health aides, licensed practical nurses, nursing aides/assistants/orderlies,* and *registered nurses,* which include: *certified nurse midwives, certified registered nurse anesthetists, clinical nurse specialists,* and *nurse practitioners.*

Nursing personnel are being hired in record numbers to fill positions which present them with increased job responsibilities. The number of home health aides in this country will more than double as the elderly population increases in number and patients are released from hospitals sooner. More advanced nurses may often be called upon to independently assess patients and suggest a course of treatment.

With the rapid changes occurring in the health care industry, nurses of all types should have no trouble finding jobs in nursing homes, HMOs, and physicians' offices. They will gain recognition as key health care providers whose role is as indispensable as that of a physician.

HOMEMAKER-HOME HEALTH AIDE

Description: Also known by the titles *home health aide, home care aide,* and *personal care attendant*, the homemaker-home health aide cares for elderly and disabled people in their own homes. Often, clients have just been released from a hospital or nursing home, or suffer from a debilitating illness which restricts independence. Duties performed by home health aides include, but are not limited to, housekeeping chores like laundry and cleaning, planning and cooking meals, bathing, dressing, and grooming the patient, reminding the patient to take medications, assisting in movement and exercise, and serving as a companion inside the home and out. Clear records are kept documenting the patient's daily activities and progress of the patient. Other health care providers such as physical therapists, registered nurses, and social workers assume a supervisory role toward homemaker-home health aides and receive direct reports from them. These supervisors are responsible for assigning the home health aides in performing specific duties at designated times.

Homemaker-home health aides are employed by home health care agencies that maintain a large pool of clients. On a typical day, a home health aide may see five or more patients, and the length of time spent with each varies from an hour to an entire afternoon. Some health aides may establish a relationship with a patient that lasts years, but variability is the norm. Work is done in the patient's home and the home health aide gains exposure to a wide range of conditions. Most days are spent one-on-one with the patient; supervisory personnel are usually not involved. Part-time, weekend, and evening work should be expected.

Education: State training requirements for homemaker-home health aides are variable and some states require no formal training. For cases where Medicare offers reimbursement, the federal government demands aides pass a 12 part competency exam, and undergo 75 hours of training. For home health aides seeking national certification, the Foundation for Hospice and Home Care award this status.

Salary, Future Outlook: Earnings depend upon experience, geographical location, and client load. In 1996, the average beginning hourly rate was from $5.25 to $6.95. For experienced home health aides, wages ranged from $5.96 to $8.29 an hour. These fees usually cover only actual time spent on the job.

In 1996, there were 697,000 jobs held by homemaker-home health aides. The outlook for this career is excellent and it is expected to be one of the fastest-growing occupations over the next ten years. Opportunities will be abundant as the elderly population increases and the high cost of institutionalized health care makes home care more appealing. Due to lower earnings, a high turnover rate is likely to persist, contributing to the demand for experienced home health aides.

Index: *American Nurses Association, National Association for Homecare, National League for Nursing*

LICENSED PRACTICAL NURSE

Description: Licensed practical nurses (LPNs), known as licensed vocational nurses (LVNs) in Texas and California, provide bedside care to patients and perform a variety of other nursing duties. Under direct supervision of registered nurses and physicians, LPNs assume the responsibilities of taking vital signs, observing patients and seeing to their comfort, collecting specimens for laboratory tests, administering medications, dressing wounds, starting IVs, and in some cases supervising nursing aides or assistants. Depending upon place of employment, some licensed practical nurses perform clerical or administrative duties.

The majority of licensed practical nurses are employed by large multi-bed facilities like hospitals and nursing homes. In 1994, 40% of LPNs worked in hospitals, 25% worked in nursing homes and 10% worked in doctor's offices and clinics. Government agencies and home health care agencies are other common places in which to find employment. Although 40-hour work weeks are typical, the nine-to-five work day is not. Patients in large facilities especially require around-the-clock monitoring by LPNs and other health care personnel.

Education: Entrance to a practical nurse training program may or may not require a high school diploma, although a diploma is definitely recommended. Of the close to 1,100 state-approved training programs in 1993, most were through vocational-technical schools and community or junior colleges. After a one-year training program, graduates must pass a licensing examination to earn the title of licensed practical nurse.

Salary, Future Outlook: According to survey data from 1996, a hospital LPN working full time earned $468 a week. Those LPNs employed in nursing homes were likely to earn $12 an hour, or approximately $624 a week. As in any career, variance is to be expected, and experienced practical nurses will usually earn more than beginners.

There were nearly 700,000 LPN jobs in 1996. Job outlook for licensed practical nurses is expected to be excellent for those seeking employment in nursing homes and about average for those interested in hospital jobs. As with all jobs in the health field, changing population dynamics will drastically boost the demand for health care providers for the elderly. If licensed practical nurses leave the field at the same rate that practical nurses are licensed, the job market will remain stable and secure.

Index: *American Health Care Association, American Nurses Association, National Federation of Licensed Practical Nurses, Inc., National League for Nursing*

NURSING AIDE/ASSISTANT/ORDERLY

Description: Nursing aides, assistants or orderlies, also referred to as hospital attendants, provide basic patient care under direct nursing supervision. Typical work activities include: attending to patients' comfort, hygiene, and meals, assisting with patient mobility, checking temperatures and vital signs, helping patients' keep room and bed tidy, and reporting any changes in patient demeanor or agility to nurses or doctors on duty. The more mundane tasks of a nursing aides may be unpleasant and trying, but these assistants often report that their days are rewarding. Especially in nursing homes, interaction with the nursing aide may be the only contact a patient has with the outside world.

Nursing aides and similar workers most often find employment in hospitals (around 50%) and nursing homes. Others may choose to work privately for families or in homes for the aged. Most nursing aides are full-time workers, but part-time shifts in the evenings and weekends are also available. For students at the high school or college level, these shifts are often the most convenient.

Education: Training requirements for nursing aides vary by state and by institution. In some instances, a high school diploma is not even required, while in others, training and experience is necessary. Nursing homes often demand at least 75 hours of training as well as an acceptable score on a proficiency exam. Training programs, predominantly at vocational-technical schools and community colleges, teach the nutrition, communication and health skills necessary to succeed as a nursing aid. Some institutions rely only on on-the-job training for their aides.

Salary, Future Outlook: Earnings of nursing aides, assistants, and orderlies varies by location, institution and experience. For most hospitals and similar medical facilities, full-time aides earned an average of $292 per week in 1996; for nursing homes the average is closer to $6.60 per hour. On a weekly basis, this translates into about $264.

In 1996, the number of nursing aide jobs in this country was 1,312,000. This number is expected to grow over the next ten years as the number of people 75 and over reaches record proportions. With the increasing need for long-term care, nursing homes will need experienced aides and will be willing to train new workers.

Index: *American Health Care Association, American Nurses Association, National League for Nursing*

REGISTERED NURSE

Description: Registered nurses (RNs) care for patients, and promote their physical, mental, and social well being. The duties performed by RNs include: monitoring patient status and progress, assisting the physician in care and rehabilitation, administering medication, and advising patients and their families on preventive health care measures. State laws and specific employer restrictions specify exactly what a registered nurse is allowed to do on the job. The title of registered nurse encompasses a wide range of specialties, among them: *hospital nurses* (bedside care in various hospital departments), *office nurses* (office and clinical care which may involve office work), *home health nurse* (nursing service in the home environment), *nursing home nurses* (long-term care nursing), *public health nurses* (community wide health education), *occupational health/industrial nurses* (worksite care), and *head nurse/nurse supervisor* (managerial and administrative responsibilities). Specialized training or experience may be necessary for some of these positions. The main difference among them, however, is simply the setting and/or members of the community toward which registered nurses choose to direct their skills. For registered nurses seeking advanced practice there are also opportunities to become **a certified nurse-midwife (CNM), certified registered nurse anesthetist (CRNA), clinical nurse specialist (CNS), and nurse practitioner (NP).** Look for specific details on each of these careers in the appropriate sections.

More than 60% of RNs are employed by hospitals, while the others may work in physicians' offices, nursing homes, schools, or government agencies. On a daily basis, an RN may be found in a hospital, patient's home, elementary school, community center, or at a worksite. The majority of registered nurses are employed full time, with hours that may extend around the clock. Hospital and nursing home positions are those most likely to provide 24-hour care, while office nurses, occupational health nurses, or public health nurses follow nine-to-five business hours.

Education: Becoming a licensed registered nurse requires graduation from an accredited nursing school and the successful completion of a national licensing examination. There are currently over 1,500 RN training programs, each falling into a category based upon the degree it awards and length of student enrollment. Approximately 70% of RNs graduate from a program which offers an associate degree (ADN). Other schools may award either a diploma or a bachelor of science degree in nursing (BSN). Associate's programs last two years and are generally offered by community or junior colleges. Diploma programs offered by hospitals last two to three years and bachelor's programs offered at colleges and universities last four to five years. RNs with a BSN degree may have more employment opportunities in administrative and community positions and someday this degree may be a standard requirement for all registered nurses. Graduate programs require its applicants to hold a bachelor of science degree.

REGISTERED NURSE - continued

Salary, Future Outlook: In 1996, full-time hospital RNs earned an average income of $697 per week. Nursing home RNs earned $15.85 per hour, which translates to approximately $634 a week, in 1996. Registered nurses employed in other settings should expect to earn a comparable salary. Experience, location and degree level may all influence salary.

There were more than 1,971,000 jobs held by registered nurses in 1996. Future prospects for RNs are likely to be better in home health care agencies and in nursing homes than in hospitals. With a rapidly growing elderly population, the demand for experienced nurses to care for them will be great. The shift in the health care system today is toward outpatient care as new technologies, cost-cutting measures, and convenience make it more practical to perform procedures in clinics, physicians' offices, and surgical centers. For advanced practice registered nurses such as certified nurse-midwives, certified registered nurse anesthetists, clinical nurse specialists, nurse practitioners, and many others, the employment outlook is good for the next ten years. Their extra training and specialization enables them to assume duties once performed exclusively by higher-priced doctors.

Index: *American Association of Occupational Health Nurses, American Health Care Association, American Nurses Association, Association of Operating Room Nurses, Inc., National Association for Home Care, National League for Nursing*

CERTIFIED NURSE-MIDWIFE

Description: Certified nurse-midwives (CMNs) are RNs with advanced training in midwifery that allows them to care for healthy expectant mothers and to provide a range of clinical services for women. They examine women during pregnancy, manage labor, deliver infants, and after birth, care for the newborn and mother. Other duties include preventive health care, counseling, prescribing medication (most states), conducting clinical research, and teaching. All 50 states have recognized nurse-midwifery as a legal profession.

Certified nurse-midwives may choose to have a private practice or may be employed in hospitals, independent birthing centers, or clinics. Hours will vary as to place of employment, although CNMs are usually on call and must be available to expectant mothers at all times.

Education: Any registered nurse may seek certified nurse-midwife status. A certification program involves up to 12 months of training, while a master's program usually takes two years. By 1999, all entrants into these CNM training programs must already have a bachelor's degree or will be awarded one upon graduation. The American College of Nurse-Midwives conducts a national examination of licensing in all 50 states.

Salary, Future Outlook: On average, the income of certified nurse-midwives will surpass the pay of a typical registered nurse. For example, in 1996, while an RN earned around $697 per week, which translates to approximately $36,244 a year, CMNs earned an average of $70,100 per year. The extra schooling and training that makes independent practice possible for CNMs is responsible for this enhanced income.

There were 5,500 practicing CNMs in 1995, and the number is projected to rise in the next few years. As explained in the section on registered nurses, advanced practice nurses – like a certified-nurse-midwife – will become more and more appealing in contrast to an expensive obstetrician/gynecologist. The established high rate of successful births at the hands of CNMs underscores their credibility and popularity.

Index: *American College of Nurse-Midwives, American Nurses Association, Maternity Center Association, National League for Nursing*

US Births Attended by a Certified Nurse-Midwife, 1996

Total US births:	**3,914,953 (1996)**
Births attended by a certified Nurse-Midwife:	**207,370**

Source: National Center for Health Statistics, 1995

CERTIFIED REGISTERED NURSE ANESTHETIST

Description: Certified registered nurse anesthetists (CRNAs) administer more than 65% of the 26 million anesthetics given to patients each year in the United States. In a role similar to that of an anesthesiologist, CRNAs monitor the vital signs and body functions of surgical patients under anesthesia.

Certified registered nurse anesthetists work in every setting in which anesthesia is delivered: traditional hospital surgical suites and obstetrical delivery rooms, dentists' offices, podiatrists, ophthalmologists, and plastic surgeons; ambulatory surgical centers; HMOs; U. S. Military and Public Health Services; and Veterans Administration medical facilities. A CRNA's work schedule will revolve around a facility's operating schedule.

Education: Programs in nurse anesthesia are opened to licensed registered nurses with a bachelor's degree and at least a year of nursing experience. These programs, of which there are less than 100 in the United States, range in length from two to three years. Graduates take a national exam to qualify as a certified registered nurse anesthetist. Biannual continuing education credits are expected of all CRNAs for rectification.

Salary, Future Outlook: In 1997, the average median salary for certified registered nurse anesthetists was $82,000. For that year, CNRAs earned the largest income of any advanced practice registered nursing group.

Because of their excellent performance and safety record, CNRAs are likely to see an increase in job opportunities in the future. There are currently over 25,000 certified nurse anesthetists, a number expected to grow as the current shift towards a cost-conscious health care system continues.

Index: *American Association of Nurse Anesthetists, American Nurses Association, National League for Nursing*

Percentage of Certified Registered Nurse Anesthetists by Employer and Setting, 1995

Hospital: 39%
CRNA/anesthesiologist group: 36%
Self/CRNA group: 15%
Other: 10%

Urban setting: 65%
Town: 34%
Rural: 1%

Source: 1996 American Association of Nurse Anesthetists membership survey

CLINICAL NURSE SPECIALIST

 Description: Clinical nurse specialists (CNSs) are registered nurses who specialize in a specific field of clinical practice. Some common areas of specialization are cardiac rehabilitation, cardiology, community health, critical care, diabetes, emergency services, gerontology, maternity and child health, medical surgical health, neonatal health, oncology, pediatric cardiology, pediatrics, psychiatric-mental health, organ transplants, and trauma.

Clinical nurse specialists work in a variety of settings, such as hospitals, doctors' offices, schools, occupational settings, and even in independent practices. Certain specialties are more suited to specific locations such as nursing homes, rehabilitative facilities, and maternity centers. For full-time workers, shifts are usually available throughout the day.

Education: Training programs for the different specialties may have different entrance requirements; most require a registered nursing license and some clinical experience in that specialty. Upon graduation, a master's degree is usually awarded and graduates prepare to take a national examination for certification.

Salary, Future Outlook: In 1996, the average annual salary for a clinical nurse specialist was $47,160, well above that of a registered nurse without advanced practice. Salary may vary by experience and employment setting.

In the next decade, all advanced practice nurses, clinical nurse specialists included, will be in demand. They provide important skills that in the past only physician specialists possessed.

Index: *American Nurses Association, National League for Nursing*

NURSE PRACTITIONER

Description: Nurse practitioners (NPs) are registered nurses who provide patient health services to maintain health, prevent illness, or deal with acute or chronic health problems. Much like clinical nurse specialists, nurse practitioners also specialize, but they do so by patient category rather than clinical setting. An NP may specialize in adult health, family health, school health, pediatric health, gerontological health, acute care, women's health, etc. Within each category, duties are similar, but the patients may differ.

The most common work settings for nurse practitioners are in hospitals and doctors' offices. Other possibilities may exist in community centers, public health departments, HMOs, schools of nursing, women's health centers, clinics, and governmental agencies. Work hours may vary, although typical full-time business hours are popular.

Education: A licensed RN may or may not need hands-on experience to be accepted into a nurse practitioner training program. Those accepted will usually receive a master's or equivalent degree upon completion. The national certification exam is individualized by specialty, and successful completion confers certified nurse practitioner status.

Salary, Future Outlook: In 1996, the average professional nurse practitioner earned $66,800. Salary may vary by location, specialty, and years of experience.

The outlook for advanced training nurses is expected to be good in the years to come. Gerontological nurse practitioners will be in demand as the elderly population increases, and family practice and pediatric nurse practitioners will be needed by HMOs to provide much of the primary health care that licensed physicians now provide.

Index: *American Academy of Nurse Practitioners, American Health Care Association, American Nurses Association, National League for Nursing*

A career in pharmacy is challenging, exciting and rewarding. New drugs and pharmaceuticals are being created and released to the public at an astonishing rate. Americans today consume a record number of prescription medications and rely on the pharmaceutical industry to prepare them accurately.

A neighborhood *pharmacist* is often a primary source of health information, keeping customers informed of new pharmaceuticals, and counseling them on drug side effects and harmful drug interactions. With the increase in drug sales, *pharmacy technicians* are being hired in record numbers to assist pharmacists and even assume some of their daily duties and responsibilities. At an advanced level, the field of pharmacology also offers excellent job opportunities. *Pharmacologists* create and test new medications that enable physicians to treat diseases more effectively.

For hardworking individuals eager to accept the challenges of an ever-changing field, pharmacy is an excellent career choice.

PHARMACIST

Description: Pharmacists are experts in the science of medicine and the art of medication therapy. They work as part of a team of health care providers to improve patient health and increase public awareness of changes in medical treatment. The specific duties of a pharmacist vary according to place of practice. Over half of the licensed pharmacists practicing today are *community pharmacists* who fill drug prescriptions, advise clients on treatment regimens, and run small neighborhood businesses. *Hospital pharmacists* provide patients with accurate drug dosages, educate the medical staff on the uses and effects of medications, monitor patients' progress and make appropriate changes in treatment as needed. *Home care pharmacists* supply patients with their medication in their home, and serve as consultants and sources of information. Pharmacists may choose to specialize in the pharmaceutical industry, enter the field of pharmacology, pursue a career in academics, or confine their practice to managed care or research companies.

Although most pharmacists work in community pharmacies or drug stores, they are also needed in hospital pharmacies, nursing homes and other similar facilities. MCOs employ pharmacists, as do pharmaceutical and industrial research companies. The federal government and pharmacy schools and colleges also hire pharmacists as staff members to remain abreast of developments in the field. Pharmacists may work 40-50 hours a week, especially those in private practice; nearly 16% of pharmacists are part-time workers.

Education: A license is required to practice pharmacy in all states and is achieved by graduating from an accredited training program, passing a state examination, and completing an internship in the field. Of the 75 institutions which awarded pharmacy degrees in 1995, some offered a BS degree in pharmacy, others offered a PharmD degree (Doctor of Pharmacy), and some offered both. The number of PharmD awarding institutions is likely to increase in the future. These programs require six years of post-high school education as opposed to the five-year BS programs. Pharmacists may choose to obtain an advanced master's or doctoral degree for some academic positions, or complete a residency in a specialized area. High school students interested in entering this field should have a strong science background and should research the admissions requirements of the individual pharmacy schools.

Salary, Future Outlook: Earnings for pharmacists vary by location, experience, and type of practice. In 1996, chain druggists averaged $61,735 per year, independent druggists earned $52,189, and hospital pharmacists earned $61,317. Pharmacists hired by pharmaceutical companies, academic institutions, and the federal government had a large salary range. Overall, the median income for a licensed salaried pharmacist in 1996 was $59,276.

In 1996, pharmacists held 172,000 jobs and the field is expected to grow at an average rate. Many jobs will be in regions with a large elderly population. Hospitals and nursing homes will hire more pharmacists as the elderly population increases to handle their tremendous prescription needs. Advances in pharmaceutical technology and diagnostic machinery will add to the number of drugs dispensed and needed in the United States. Job growth may be hampered by an increased use of automated machines and pharmacy technicians to fill prescriptions and dispense information.

Index: *American Association of Colleges of Pharmacy, American Pharmaceutical Association, American Society of Health System Pharmacists*

PHARMACY TECHNICIAN

Description: Pharmacy technicians function as support personnel for pharmacists. State regulations determine the exact duties that a pharmacy technician is allowed to perform. They may straighten and organize the pharmacy, assist in updating patient records, keep the pharmacy fully stocked, and complete prescription labels under the direction of a pharmacist. Some may also receive prescription orders and contact physicians to sanction order refills.

Pharmacy technicians are hired in the same settings where pharmacists work. Neighborhood pharmacies, hospitals, independent laboratories, federal agencies and pharmaceutical companies all employ technicians. A technician may be employed on a part-time basis, although many choose to make their work a full-time career.

Education: The educational requirements for pharmacy technicians vary according to the type and extent of duties they are hired to perform. Some who are merely assistants and work only under direct supervision may be hired without any formal training. However, the majority of pharmacy technicians attend a community college or vocational-technical school where they are trained in the fundamentals of pharmaceutical science. An associate's degree is the most significant degree awarded for this field, and it takes two years to obtain.

The average salary earned by a pharmacy technician varies based on years of experience, work location, and extent of duties. Technicians tend to earn salaries in the range of $20,000-$30,000 a year.

Salary, Future Outlook: In 1996, there were 83,000 pharmacy technicians working in all facets of the health care industry. Over the next ten years, this will be a field of rapid growth as the demand for prescription medication increases and institutions attempt to contain costs. The pharmacist's role will be restructured to focus more on patient consultation, while their basic tasks will be left for technicians. As long as patient safety is not compromised by technical mistakes, the pharmacy technician's job outlook will be one of the best in health care.

Index: *American Association of Pharmacy Technicians, American Pharmaceutical Association*

1996 Profile of Pharmacy Students

B.S. Program enrollment:	20,562
Pharm.D. enrollment:	3,008
Full time graduate school enrollment:	2,876
Ph.D. enrollment:	2,174
M.S. enrollment:	702
B.S. degrees awarded:	6,168
Pharm.D. degrees awarded:	1,835
Post B.S. Pharm.D. degrees awarded:	732
Ph.D. degrees awarded:	304
M.S. degrees awarded:	422

Source: American Association of Colleges of Pharmacy, Profile of Pharmacy Students 1996

PHARMACOLOGISTS

Description: Pharmacologists specialize in the research and development of drugs to treat or prevent disease and prolong human life. While pharmacists prescribe medication to patients stricken with disease, pharmacologists work to develop new drug products. In designing new drug therapies, pharmacologists must painstakingly test the drug's effects on all body systems, note any harmful side effects, ascertain proper dosage information, and conduct studies on live subjects. Pharmacologists may specialize in the sub-fields of *neuropharmacology, cardiovascular pharmacology, molecular pharmacology, biochemical pharmacology, endocrine pharmacology, clinical pharmacology, chemotherapy,* and *veterinary pharmacology.*

Pharmacologists are usually employed in the research laboratories of pharmaceutical companies and universities, or as instructors in academic institutions. They spend large amounts of time in the laboratory and may need to work some evening hours and on weekends. The federal government also employs pharmacologists to serve in the Food and Drug Administration, National Institutes of Health, and other similar agencies. Pharmacologists put so much time and effort into their education that they almost always take a full-time position.

Education: All pharmacologists have a PhD in pharmacology from a medical school, university, or pharmacy school. After obtaining a bachelor's degree with a major in the sciences, students interested in pharmacology need four to six more years of graduate schooling and research to receive their doctorate. It is not uncommon for experienced pharmacologists to hold multiple degrees, depending on where they were schooled. Many pharmacologists with a PhD choose to complete up to four additional years of research training to gain more experience and credibility in the field.

Salary, Future Outlook: Advances in today's pharmaceutical industry will undoubtedly translate into an increased demand for experienced laboratory pharmacologists. Pharmacologists will also be called upon to assume the role of keeping physicians, nurses and pharmacists educated about changes in the field. For these reasons, the field of pharmacology is likely to experience significant growth over the next ten years.

Index: *American College of Clinical Pharmacology, American Society for Pharmacology and Experimental Therapeutics*

PUBLIC HEALTH

Workers in the public health field are concerned with community-wide health care and deal with populations rather than individuals. Some populations may include specific occupational workers, members of a specific age group, or any group of people who share a common risk factor for disease or injury.

Public health professionals identify communities or groups at risk for disease, develop public policy initiatives that address global, national, and community health problems, and work to ensure that all individuals receive adequate health care. Although all public health specialists work for the ultimate goal of health promotion and disease prevention, they differ in their methods. *Biomedical and laboratory practitioners, health services administrators, nutritionists, environmental scientists, and occupational health and safety specialists* are workers who may function within or outside the public health context. *Biostatisticians, epidemiologists, health educators, international health specialists, and pubic health program specialists* are more exclusive to the public health field.

For public health professionals of all types, employment opportunities are far-reaching and are increasingly extending into all other health care fields.

BIOMEDICAL AND LABORATORY PRACTITIONER

Description: Workers in this field include scientific laboratory specialists who investigate health and disease using lab technology. They may be specialists in *microbiology, parasitology, laboratory practice, pathobiology/pathology, virology, biology sanitation, biomedical laboratory science, physiology, chemistry sanitation*, or *immunology*.

BIOSTATISTICIAN

Description: Biostatisticians apply mathematics and statistics to the compilation, analysis, and reporting of health-related information. They might estimate what percentage of a certain population is likely to develop a disease, consider the likelihood of disease transmission, and look at data from clinical trials and studies to determine the best method of intervention. Biostatisticians also use their expertise in sampling and statistical significance to assist health investigators designing studies. They may specialize in demography or health data systems/vital statistics.

ENVIRONMENTAL SCIENTIST

Description: Environmental health workers plan, develop, implement, and evaluate standards and systems to improve the quality of the physical environment as it affects health. They also manage environmental health problems and promote public awareness of the need to prevent and eliminate environmental health hazards. Specialists within this field may concentrate on food protection, radiological health, environmental health, environmental medicine, sanitation, water quality/resources, air pollution/resources, noise pollution, toxicology, and solid waste management.

EPIDEMIOLOGIST

Description: Epidemiologists analyze the occurrence and distribution of diseases within a population by determining the possible vector or mode of disease transmission, and examining the efficiency of intervention programs. Epidemiologists may specialize in infectious disease, chronic disease, environmental/occupational epidemiology, psycho/social epidemiology, health care evaluation, or human genetics.

HEALTH EDUCATOR

Description: Health educators plan, implement, and evaluate the effects of educational programs designed to support and modify health-related behaviors. They promote good health by educating the public about the causes of disease and the means of prevention on a community-wide level. Public health workers within this area may specialize in the behavioral sciences, public health education, school health education, and communication theory/health media.

HEALTH SERVICES ADMINISTRATOR

Description: In ways similar to the health services administrators of hospitals and HMOs, those in public health deal with the organization, policy formation, financing, and economics involved in a community-wide health care system. They may specialize in health services administration, health planning, health policy, hospital administration, operations research and systems, health economics, health law and general public health.

INTERNATIONAL HEALTH SPECIALIST

Description: International public health specialists apply all public health specializations to improving standards in developing countries. This includes ensuring that basic health and nutritional requirements are met, identifying any endemic diseases and their modes of transmission, working towards community-wide sanitation and environmental safety, and educating the country's citizens on the importance of health maintenance.

NUTRITIONIST

Description: Nutritionists in public health are concerned with human nutrition and the effect of nutrients on a population's health. Specialties include experts in nutrition science, biochemistry, and community nutrition.

OCCUPATIONAL SAFETY AND HEALTH SPECIALIST

Description: Occupational health and safety specialists identify and prevent accident-producing or hazardous conditions and practices in the workplace. They investigate hazards in the work environment and seek ways to prevent or control them through worksite wellness programs. Specialists may focus on occupational health, occupational medicine, industrial hygiene and safety, or ergonomics, which is the applied science of equipment design intended to reduce operator fatigue and discomfort.

Schools of Public Health Graduate Salaries by Specialty, 1996

Specialty	Salary
Biomedical and laboratory practice:	$54,000
Biostatistician:	$45,000
Environmental sciences:	$95,000
Epidemiology:	$90,000
Health education:	$58,000
Health services administration:	$107,000
International health:	$58,000
Nutrition:	$48,000
Occupational safety and health:	$84,000
Public health and program management:	$68,000

Source: Association of Schools of Public Health, 1996

PUBLIC HEALTH PROGRAM SPECIALIST

Description: Public health program specialists plan, implement and evaluate interventions to identify those at risk from a specified health problem, and try to prevent such health problems. Specialists work in public health practice, mental health, public health/community dentistry, public health nursing, preventive medicine, aging/gerontology, and maternal and child health.

Public health professionals often work for state or federal public health departments. Federal agencies such as the National Institutes of Health, Centers for Disease Control, Department of Health and Human Services, and branches of the armed forces, employ public health workers of all specialties. The World Health Organization uses public health personnel to monitor and maintain global health, and almost every nation has individual public health policy makers. Private industrial companies, hospitals, pharmaceutical companies, and research institutions may also hire public health specialists to ensure health safety standards. Voluntary health agencies (VHAs), such as the American Cancer Society, the American Heart Association, and Easter Seals, often employ public health professionals to run programs and assume administrative roles. VHAs educate the public on disease prevention and organize community programs for disease victims and their families. Additionally, universities and schools employ public health professionals to teach at the undergraduate and graduate level. Public health specialists may work in a laboratory, office building, school, workplace, and nursing home, in the United States or overseas. Work schedules vary widely.

Education: Although many colleges and universities award a bachelor's degree in public health, most advanced positions require a master's degree (MPH). There are currently 30 schools in the United States which are recognized and accredited by the Association of Schools of Public Health (ASPH). Not all schools offer programs in every specialty, but most will have course work that touches on them. Graduate students must take core courses in biostatistics, epidemiology, health administration, environmental health, and behavioral sciences before narrowing their focus to one specialty. Admission into schools of public health is competitive, and a strong applicant will normally have some employment experience in the field. Applicants with degrees in another field such as law, medicine, business, or education may be more attractive to admissions committees. Typically, a master's program in public health takes up to two years to complete and some graduates may then pursue training at the doctoral level.

Salary, Future Outlook: Public health professionals' salaries vary by specialty, experience, geographic location, and level of education. The average salary among all specialties was $70,700 in 1996.

Health care today emphasizes preventive medicine. Thus, epidemiological, nutritional, and educational data offered by public health specialists will continue to be in demand. As the baby boomer generation reaches retirement age and the nation's population dynamics shift dramatically, more public health officials trained in the area of gerontological and long-term care will be needed. Environmental and occupational health continue to be of prime public interest, and specialists in these fields can expect diverse job opportunities.

Index: *Agency for Health Care Policy and Research, American Association for Health Education, American College Health Association, American School Health Association, American Statistical Association, Association of Schools of Public Health, National Association of Community Health Centers*

The fields of science and engineering impact directly on medicine and health care. Health scientists are research scientists whose work in biology, chemistry, and genetics is crucial to a physician's understanding of disease processes and the effects of medication. *Biomedical engineers* and *biomedical equipment technicians* invent, produce, and maintain intricate equipment and machinery which are used to cure illnesses and save lives. *Anatomists*, often medical doctors themselves, are experts in the science of anatomy, teaching students the basic systems and structures of the body, and applying their knowledge to current medical research projects. *Food scientists* and *occupational health and safety specialists* work on a larger scale to ensure the health and safety of society as a whole. The work done by these professionals is rewarding and affects everyone's lives, directly or indirectly.

Over the last century, the advances made by health care scientists and engineers have been astounding, transforming the practice of medicine into a more accurate science and helping to eliminate diseases, change unhealthy behaviors, and produce new medical treatments. These fields challenge the brightest minds to match and exceed the work of their predecessors.

ANATOMIST

Description: Anatomists investigate organisms and their structures to discover their form and how they work. Anatomists teach medical, dental, and allied health students about the structure and function of the human body. As researchers, they may be involved in any aspect of biomedical research, from problems at the molecular level to those of the entire body. Their work may involve the medical fields of neuroanatomical or developmental human anatomy, or the biological fields of anthropology, embryology, genetics, endocrinology and others.

Anatomists work primarily in the classrooms of medical colleges and universities or in research laboratories. Some may be employed in hospitals as physicians or work in veterinary clinics and laboratories. It is not unusual for an anatomist to work more than 40 hours a week, depending on the place of employment. They may split their time between the classroom and the laboratory.

Education: To be a practicing anatomist requires either an MD degree or a PhD. Many anatomists hold doctorate degrees in dental, osteopathic, and veterinary medicine, and most medical, veterinary, and osteopathic training schools have anatomy departments that provide students with instruction and advice on research projects in the field.

Salary, Future Outlook: The work done by these professionals will remain important even in an age of radical technological advances and scientific breakthroughs, because anatomists provide the foundation for advanced medical techniques and practices. Almost every medical school requires its first-year students to take an introductory course in anatomy. Additionally, anatomists are finding a niche in biomedical research and will be called upon to apply their expert knowledge of the human body to other subjects, as well.

Index: *American Association of Anatomists*

BIOMEDICAL ENGINEER

Description: Biomedical engineers apply engineering techniques to solve biological and medical problems. They may design patient care equipment, such as dialysis machines and cardiac pacemakers, or develop equipment to measure various body functions. These engineers may also carry out research in the medical field which provides ideas for innovative projects. Biomedical engineering includes specialty fields such as *bioinstrumentation; biomaterials; biomechanics; cellular biomedical engineering, tissue and genetic engineering; clinical engineering; medical imaging; orthopedic bioengineering; rehabilitation engineering*; and *systems physiology*. Often, these specialists work together on projects, sharing information, techniques and ideas.

The biomedical engineer may work in a variety of medical and technical settings. Most jobs are in hospitals, industrial manufacturing companies, private and university-level research facilities, medical schools, and the government. Depending upon the work setting, hours may vary, although the 40-hour work week is a typical option.

Education: Most biomedical engineers begin their training in a college-level engineering program. These programs are offered by colleges and universities all over the country and usually last five years. Students may specialize in either biomedical engineering or another engineering field with an emphasis on the biomedical sciences. Although not always required for employment, students may wish to enroll in a master's or doctoral program after receiving a degree in biomedical engineering. Others may simply join the workforce and get valuable hands-on experience in the field.

Salary, Future Outlook: The future promises to be exciting for biomedical engineers. Enhanced applications in computer technology will aid engineers who monitor patients in surgery and under other stressful conditions. Technological developments with lasers, new constructive materials, and automated systems will become more commonplace as engineers improve existing diagnostic and therapeutic techniques. With the current downsizing of hospital and other health care employees, biomedical engineers will be in demand to create efficient and inexpensive computerized replacements for actual health workers.

Index: *Association for the Advancement of Medical Instrumentation, Biomedical Engineering Society*

Number of Science and Engineering Doctorates Awarded by Year, 1996

Year	Number
1990:	22, 868
1991:	24,023
1992:	24,675
1993:	25,443
1994:	26,205
1995:	26,535
1996:	27,230

Source: National Science Foundation, Division of Science Resources Studies Science and Engineering Doctorate Awards: 1996 (NSF 96-329)

BIOMEDICAL EQUIPMENT TECHNICIAN

Description: Biomedical equipment technicians (BMETs) are the professionals trained to ensure that medical instruments and equipment function properly. They may work on diagnostic instruments such as ultrasound and electrocardiograph (EKG) machines, life support equipment such as ventilators and dialysis machines, and virtually any other type of medical equipment found in a health care facility. BMETs may be called to fix broken instruments, install equipment in a new facility, or simply conduct periodic testing to ensure proper functioning of biomedical equipment. BMETs may specialize in general biomedical equipment, radiological equipment, or clinical equipment.

Biomedical equipment technicians are often employed by hospitals and large medical centers, or they may work in medical schools, research institutions, and federal agencies. Biomedical equipment manufacturers often maintain a staff of BMETs to attend to technical problems in the field and ensure that their instruments are being used properly. These technicians often work a standard 40-hour week, but occasionally are on-call around the clock to attend to emergency situations.

Education: There are training courses for biomedical equipment technicians offered at certificate through bachelor's degree levels. Many community colleges and vocational-technical schools offer two-year associate's degree programs in biomedical equipment technology, and some offer a more general program in electronics technology. The International Certification Commission for Clinical Engineering and Biomedical Technology (ICC) is the certifying body of biomedical equipment technicians and sets the requirements for the certification examination. According to the ICC, eligible certification candidates are those who have four years of full-time experience as a BMET; an associate's degree in biomedical equipment technology and two years of work experience as a BMET; or an associate's degree in electronics technology and three years of work experience as a BMET.

Salary, Future Outlook: As long as biomedical engineers continue to create new instruments for the medical field, the demand will be great for biomedical equipment technicians to maintain their upkeep. Hospital and other health service administrators know that by paying technicians to perform preventive maintenance, they will avoid costly service bills. Technicians with the best employment prospects will be those who have experience and familiarity with modern equipment.

Index: *Association for the Advancement of Medical Instrumentation*

FOOD SCIENTIST

Description: Food scientists, also referred to as food technologists and food engineers, apply science to the selection, preservation, processing, packaging, distribution, and use of safe, nutritious, and wholesome food. They may develop new foods or new ways to make them, check the safety of food additives and ingredients, or investigate the effects of processing and packaging methods. Food scientists may assist developing countries suffering from a shortage of nutritious food because of famine, poor sanitation and food preservation, or insufficient processing. They may also serve as researchers dedicated to improving current food science practices or as teachers of food science.

Food scientists are employed throughout the United States in a variety of capacities. Many jobs are available through governmental agencies, such as the Department of Agriculture, Department of Health and Human Services, and even the World Health Organization or United Nations. However, most food scientists are employed in private industry and food manufacturing, processing and distribution sectors. There are many job opportunities in research and academia. The typical work week is 40 hours for most food scientist, but this may vary by employer or by work setting.

Education: Most jobs in food science require at least a four-year bachelor's degree in food science or a related field. The Institute of Food Technologists has approved over 50 college and university level programs which award the bachelor of science degree in food science. Many institutions offer master's and doctoral level programs for students interested in furthering their education or specializing within food science. Upper level research and teaching positions are often only open to candidates with their doctorate.

Salary, Future Outlook: Professionals in the food science field often earn a higher salary than other professionals of comparable schooling. An average bachelor's degree graduate earned just over $24,000 in 1997, while those working as a food scientist in a federal capacity made closer to $55,200. At the master's and doctoral levels, salaries are substantially higher and may even reach the triple digits for upper level teaching and research positions.

Today, the public is more health-conscious and nutritionally educated than ever before, and food scientists will likely have the best job prospects of all agricultural scientists.

Index: *Institute of Food Technologists*

HEALTH SCIENTIST

Description: The term health scientist refers to all biological, medical, and non-biological scientists who work to promote health and study health issues. These scientists are predominantly researchers, but may also teach or work in an industrial capacity. *Biochemists* study the inherent chemical processes that are responsible for such things as sustaining life, governing metabolism, and controlling reproduction in living organisms. Botanists are biologists who specialize in all forms of plant life, including plant disease, photosynthesis, and plant identification. *Chemists* in the health care industry help develop drugs, sterile synthetic products, and other items which aid the advancement of medicine. *Ecologists* study the effects of the environment on human, animal, and plant life. Geneticists are medical doctors who track genetic disease, study inheritance and multiple births, pioneer genetic testing, and work at the molecular level to map genes and investigate chromosomal abnormalities. Health physicists study the effect of radiation on living things and expose the hazards of nuclear and radioactive waste. Medical scientists are biologists who engage in all types of biomedical research, including disease studies and drug testing. A *microbiologist* studies microscopic organisms and may specialize in the areas of bacteriology, immunology, microbial physiology, mycology, parasitology, or virology.

Depending on the specific field in which a health scientist is employed, the work setting will vary. Most biological and non-biological scientists work in laboratories or in academics as faculty members. Medical scientists may work in hospitals or in the drug industry, and some are licensed medical doctors. Government agencies such as the Department of Agriculture, Department of Health and Human Services, and Centers for Disease Control often hire health scientists. The medical research done by health scientists is often of prime interests to voluntary health agencies (VHAs). Often, VHAs will indirectly "hire" health scientists by funding their research projects. Non-traditional work in primitive conditions may also be a part of these fields, especially when scientists study organisms in their native environment. While traditional academic or laboratory scientists work standard office hours, those engaged in non-traditional projects may have a modified schedule.

Education: Virtually every college and university offers bachelor's degree programs in biological or related sciences. While a bachelor's degree qualifies an individual for employment in non-research, technical, and assistant capacities, all other positions are generally reserved for those with a master's or doctoral degree. These upper level programs are generally specialized to a single scientific discipline and can be found at major universities across the country. A master's degree qualifies one to perform applied research or assume jobs at the management level, and all college level teaching and independent research jobs require a PhD Medical scientists must have their PhD and to the extent it facilitates their work in the field, many also pursue an MD degree.

Salary, Future Outlook: The salaries of health scientists vary by scientific discipline, level of education, and years of experience. In 1996, the average earnings for all biological scientists were $36,300 while medical scientists earned an average of $34,300. Within the federal government, microbiologists earned $58,700, ecologists earned $52,700, and geneticists earned $62,700.

In 1996, biological and medical scientists held 118,000 jobs. Although overall employment statistics for health scientists are expected to be better than the national average, there will be competition for higher level research and teaching jobs. However, rapid advances in medicine and biotechnology will benefit patients and are good for industrial profits, and scientists will have no shortage of jobs. The health industry in particular will continue large scale research projects — dealing with AIDS, genetics, and cancer. Increased interest in the environment will lead to more research in this area, and medical scientists will continue to concentrate on improved human health.

Index: *American Association of Anatomists, American Association for Clinical Chemistry, American Society for Microbiology*

OCCUPATIONAL SAFETY SPECIALIST

Description: The broad title of occupational safety specialist includes all occupational health and safety professionals who detect and identify accident-producing or hazardous conditions. They evaluate and communicate the severity of the hazards, and develop systems to control or eliminate them. occupational safety specialists may detect and correct industrial hazards such as radiation or pollution, redesign machinery to protect against worker injury, and investigate on the job psychological forces which may threaten employee health. Once a hazard control program is in place, occupational safety specialists monitor its effectiveness by observing the modified job site and analyzing statistical data on worker health. These professionals encompass many different occupational groups and job titles, including *industrial hygienists, safety engineers, occupational health and safety technologists, environmental engineers,* and *risk managers.*

Occupational safety specialists work in a variety of settings. Common employers are insurance companies, the government, construction and manufacturing outlets, and consulting firms. Colleges and universities with programs in this field often include industrial hygienists and other occupational safety workers on their faculties. On a daily basis, an occupational safety specialist may work in an office or in the field, and in both cases spend an average of eight hours on the job.

Education: Colleges and universities all over the country offer programs which qualify graduates to enter the occupational safety field. At the undergraduate level, students in this field typically seek a degree in science or engineering. While a bachelor's degree may be sufficient for some entry level positions, a master's degree increases the likelihood of securing a job. Graduate degrees are offered in more specialized fields such as occupational health and/or safety technology, safety engineering, and industrial hygiene. There are currently 21 master's level programs in industrial hygiene that are accredited by the Accreditation Board for Engineering and Technology. The American Board of Industrial Hygiene is one body that certifies safety professionals who have completed the necessary training and experience in occupational safety at an advanced level.

Salary, Future Outlook: Workplace safety is likely to continue to be a priority for employers, employees, and the public. With technological advances, complex automated machinery will dominate the factories of the industrial world and present occupational safety specialists with added responsibilities. The public's interest in the environment will lead it to rely on occupational safety specialists to prevent industrial pollution and other irreversibly damaging practices. Employers will have to adhere to tougher governmental guidelines regarding occupational and public safety, and will seek safety teams to troubleshoot in the workplace. For these reasons, a career in occupational safety enforcement will undoubtedly become a more popular choice among graduates.

Index: *American Industrial Hygiene Association, American Society of Safety Engineers, National Environmental Health Association*

The practice of health care in this country has been improved largely by the technological revolution, which has made medical treatments more effective and has greatly improved the diagnostic capabilities of health care providers. Today, it is possible to observe internal organs, mechanically ventilate a patient's lungs, and test the functioning of the brain non-invasively. The health care professionals responsible for using this equipment properly are highly trained in both the technical and medical aspects of their respective fields.

Cardiovascular and *electroneurodiagnostic technicians and technologists* monitor the functioning of the heart and brain, respectively. *Diagnostic medical sonographers, nuclear medicine technologists*, and *radiologic technologists* specialize in using technological equipment for preventive diagnostic imaging and monitoring disease progression. *Radiation therapists* administer radiation to patients with cancer, respiratory therapists treat patients afflicted with lung or breathing disorders, and *surgical technologists* maintain the sterility of all surgical equipment and assist the physician during procedures.

The professionals who work with the advanced equipment used in medical centers today are as important as the pieces of equipment themselves. A career in any of these fields is likely to challenge the most inquisitive of individuals and satisfy those for whom patient contact is a priority.

CARDIOVASCULAR TECHNICIAN AND TECHNOLOGIST

Description: Cardiovascular technicians and technologists are trained technical professionals who specialize in cardiac (heart) and vascular (blood vessel) functioning. Most technicians and technologists can be found in one of the following special categories. *Electrocardiograph technicians* (ECG or EKG technicians) use electrodes to connect patients to a machine that monitors the electrical properties of their heart. Technicians with advanced skills may perform Holter monitor testing in which the heart is monitored by a small mobile machine for 24 hours. Stress testing allows the EKG technician to observe heart functioning while the patient walks on a treadmill. *Cardiology technologists* are cardiovascular technologists specializing in invasive heart procedures. They perform cardiac catheterization procedures such as angioplasty, in which a catheter is inserted into the heart. Noninvasive technologists called *echocardiographers* use ultrasound to create images of the heart for diagnostic purposes.

Cardiovascular technologists and technicians are employed wherever cardiovascular testing is performed. All hospital cardiology departments, cardiologist's offices, cardiac rehabilitation centers, and diagnostic centers need experienced technical workers to perform tests ranging from the rudimentary to the most complex. The majority of technologists and technicians work full-time, 40-hour weeks, with some filling evening and weekend shifts as needed.

Education: Technician positions encompassing basic EKG, Holter monitor, and stress tests may be given to someone without previous formal training, as 8-16 weeks of on-the-job training will suffice. A student technician may also enroll in a one year certificate programs where the same skills are taught. Cardiovascular technologists require specialized instruction and must complete two years of study at an accredited community or junior college.

Salary, Future Outlook: In 1997, a cardiovascular technician earned an average of $20,200. Cardiovascular technologists, due to their extra schooling and advanced training, earned an average of $33,600.

The total number of technicians and technologists employed is approximately 30,000. Job outlook is expected to be good for technologists, whose patient load will grow as the number of elderly individuals in the country increases. EKG technicians specializing in Holter monitoring and stress testing will still be needed, but other health care workers will increasingly perform resting EKG's.

Index: *Alliance of Cardiovascular Professionals, American Society of Echocardiography, Commission on Accreditation of Allied Health Programs*

DIAGNOSTIC MEDICAL SONOGRAPHER

Description: Diagnostic medical sonographers use high-frequency sound waves (ultrasound) to create body images that show the shape and composition of body tissues. These images assist physicians in diagnosing disease, injury, or other physical conditions. The sonographer will first record patient history, position the patient for ultrasound testing, and explain the procedure in detail. Although many sonographers are trained to use ultrasound on all body parts, some may specialize in neurosonography (brain), vascular sonography (blood vessels), echocardiography (heart), abdominal sonography (abdominal cavity), obstetrics/gynecological sonography (female reproductive system), or ophthalmologic sonography (eye). As with other radiologic technologists, diagnostic medical sonographers work under the direct supervision of a physician and must follow orders explicitly.

While most diagnostic medical sonographers are employed in hospital departments such as radiology, cardiology, obstetrics, and vascular surgery, they may also be hired to work in other locations. Diagnostic imaging centers, physicians' offices, MCOs, and other medical facilities also employ sonographers, but to a lesser extent. Over 50% of sonographers work in a full-time position and hours may include evening, weekend or on call shifts, depending on location of employment.

Education: For those interested in a career in sonography, formal training is essential. Different facilities offer programs of varying lengths, and there are approximately 65 programs. Generally, admission to one of these programs requires a high school diploma and some experience in a health-related profession. Training options included a one-year certificate program, a two-year associates program, or a four-year baccalaureate program. Sonographers need to be licensed in some states, and will often opt to become certified by the American Registry of Diagnostic Medical Sonographers.

Salary, Future Outlook: In 1997, ultrasound technologists earned an average of $36,100 while radiologic technologists averaged $28,800. Actual earnings varied on either side of this median value, and often were based on years of experience in the field or work location.

With the advent of many new ultrasound procedures expected over the next ten years, the demand for sonographers is likely to grow and be greater than the demand for radiologic technologists. More physicians' offices and managed care facilities are likely to hire diagnostic medical sonographers, and may surpass hospitals as their primary employers. The high costs of new ultrasound procedures and equipment may serve to stifle job growth to a small extent.

Index: *American College of Radiology, Commission on Accreditation of Allied Health Education Programs, Society of Diagnostic Medical Sonographers*

ELECTRONEURODIAGNOSTIC TECHNOLOGIST

Description: Electroneurodiagnostic technologists operate electroencephalograph (EEG) machines to record electrical brain activity and diagnose brain disorders such as stroke and tumors. These technologists obtain complete patient histories before any procedure, affix electrodes in the appropriate positions on the patient's head, and monitor instrumentational feedback. Originally referred to as *EEG technologists*, electroneurodiagnostic technologists perform many types of complex testing beyond the basic, resting EEG. EEG services are requested in the operating room while a patient is exposed to anesthesia, and are conducted over a 24-hour period of ambulatory monitoring. *Evoked potential test specialists* measure a patient's sensory response to a particular stimulus, and *nerve conduction test specialists* measure the length of time for nerve impulse transduction to a muscle. Sleep disorder experts in the electroneurodiagnostic field who monitor brain wave, respiratory, and heart activity during stages of sleep are called *polysomnographic technologists*. Some technologists perform administrative and office work in addition to their diagnostic duties. The majority of electroneurodiagnostic technologists are employed in hospital neurology departments. Neurologic doctors' and surgeons' offices, diagnostic sleep centers, mental health facilities, and MCOs also hire these EEG experts. Most technologists, with the exception of some hospital and sleep center employees, will work a standard business hour work week. Testing is usually conducted in a laboratory setting, although hospital patients often have personal visits from technologists in their hospital room.

Education: Depending on the employer, training on the job may be sufficient enough to qualify for most technologist positions. Often, if one has had work experience in other areas of the hospital, on the job training is appropriate. Some facilities require their electroneurodiagnostic technologists to have passed a community college or hospital based formal training program. Approximately 14 accredited programs currently exist. They ranged in length from one to two years, and awarded an associate's degree or certificate upon graduation. Registry boards in the field offer the credentials Registered EEG Technologist, Registered Evoked Potential Technologist, and Registered Polysomnographic Technologist. Advanced levels of employment may exist in research, teaching, and laboratory management.

Salary, Future Outlook: In 1997, the average full-time electroneurodiagnostic technologist earned $26,800. The actual salary ranged from a low of $23,200 to more than $30,000. Variance was due to type of EEG specialization, employer, and experience within the field.

With the multitude of technologic and scientific advances expected over the next ten years, employment prospects for electroneurodiagnostic professionals are likely to be better than for most fields. There were only 6,400 electroneurodiagnostic jobs in 1996, but the demand for EEG testing is likely to increase as the elderly population increases. Hospitals will continue to employ the greatest number of technologists, but more openings will exist in neurology clinics and doctors' offices.

Index: *American Society of Electroneurodiagnostic Technologists, Commission on Accreditation of Allied Health Education Programs*

NUCLEAR MEDICINE TECHNOLOGIST

Description: Nuclear medicine technologists, under a physician's supervision, use small amounts of radiopharmaceuticals to diagnose and treat diseases. Radiopharmaceuticals, introduced into the body via injection, inhalation, or ingestion, aid in the diagnostic imaging of such organs as the heart, lungs, liver, kidneys and brain. These radioactive tracers are useful because they are attracted by certain internal organs and emit easily detectable high energy rays. Using sensitive instrumentation, the technologist can obtain a useful image of the structure and function of the specific organ in question. Technologists are also concerned with the safe storage and disposal of these radioactive materials. They may prepare and administer the materials, operate nuclear instruments, position patients for diagnostic procedures, and prepare information received from the tests for the doctor's interpretation. Technologists must monitor radiation levels at all times to ensure the safety of their patients and themselves.

Close to 90% of all nuclear medicine technologists are employed in hospitals. All others find positions in physicians' offices, imaging centers, and similar facilities. A 40-hour work week is standard for nuclear medicine technologists. Part-time shifts may also be available, with weekend and evening hours possible.

Education: Most nuclear medicine technology positions are filled by those who have completed a formal training program. A one-year certificate program may be offered by a hospital to train those in other health-related, technological, or diagnostic imaging fields. A two-year certificate program or a two-year community college-based associate's program may be options for those interested in more training. Finally, four-year colleges and universities also offer training in nuclear medicine technology. There are approximately 120 accredited training programs. Some states require licensure, and applicants who are certified may be more attractive to certain employers.

Salary, Future Outlook: The average nuclear medicine technologist earned $36,100 in 1997, with salaries ranging from $28,044 to $41,598. Although these statistics were representative of a full-time worker, part-time employees may receive an hourly wage or receive shift variable pay rates.

The field of nuclear medicine technology is a small one, with 13,000 workers in 1996. As the elderly population grows and an increase in diagnostic tests is expected, the services of nuclear medicine technologists will be in demand. With advances in diagnostic science and the expanded use of radiopharmaceuticals, procedures are likely to be more expensive and may not appeal to cost-conscious hospitals and HMOs. For these reasons, the number of job openings in the field may be kept small, even as the demand grows.

Index: *Society of Nuclear Medicine*

RADIATION THERAPY TECHNOLOGIST

Description: Radiation therapy technologists, also known as radiation therapists, comprise another subset of workers known as **radiologic technologists**. These professionals administer doses of radiation to treat patients afflicted with cancer. By applying radiation in the form of X-rays, gamma rays and electron beams to specific body parts, the radiation therapist attempts to halt the spread of disease or offer relief from symptoms. Radiation therapy technologists deliver the course of radiation, give support and information to the patient, and work closely with oncologists to weigh treatment options and monitor patient progress. Cancer patients and their families often develop a meaningful relationship with these health care providers over the course of their treatment.

While most radiation therapists are employed in hospitals, many others work in clinics and research facilities. Forty-hour work weeks are common among these technologists, and may include non-business hours. The workload for these professionals is often emotionally draining, due to their involvement with children and adults who are seriously ill.

Education: Formal training programs are the most popular means of entrance into this field. In 1995, there were 125 accredited radiation therapy programs offered in hospitals, colleges, and vocational-technical institutes. A training option for radiographers interested in pursuing a career in radiation therapy is the one-year certificate program. For others not already involved in the radiologic field, training options include a two-year hospital certificate program, a two- to three-year associate's degree, or a four-year bachelor's degree from a college or university. Licensure of radiation therapists was required by 26 states in 1995, and most employers prefer the therapist to be voluntarily certified. The American Registry of Radiologic Technologists offers the ARRT certification for radiation therapy technologists as well as for radiographers. A biannual continuing education requirement must also be filled by these technologists.

Salary, Future Outlook: In 1997, a radiation therapy technologist earned an average of $37,300 — significantly higher that the average income for all radiologic technologists ($28,800). As with most other careers, the number of years in the field will affect one's salary, as will training level, scope of responsibility, and the employer.

As the number of elderly rises significantly, more diagnoses of cancer will be made. Developments in the science of cancer detection and radiation treatment, when combined with the large number of new cancer cases, should translate into an increased demand for radiation therapy technologists. Physicians' offices and private clinics will hire the most new therapists, and hospitals will need to continually refill their therapist positions with new workers. Experienced workers with familiarity in other radiologic techniques will be the most successful in finding employment.

Index: *American College of Radiology, American Society of Radiologic Technologists*

RADIOLOGIC TECHNOLOGIST

Description: The title of radiologic technologist covers a wide range of health care professionals who make use of radiation for diagnostic imaging. *Radiographers*, who most commonly produce X-rays of the body, are responsible for preparing patients for the procedure and developing the film for analysis by a physician. More experienced radiographers may administer fluoroscopies, which when taken orally, enhance soft-tissue imaging. *CT technologists* use computerized tomography to view patients cross-sectionally. *Magnetic resonance imaging (MRI) technologists* are also radiographers, but they are skilled in using magnets and radio waves instead of radiation to create images. All radiologic technologists are under the direct supervision of a physician. Sonographers and radiation therapy technologists comprise two more subsets of radiologic technologists. More information on **diagnostic medical sonographers** and **radiation therapy technologists** is given in their designated sections.

Hospitals employ the largest number of radiologic technologists, approximately 60 %. Other sites that employ radiologic technologists include physicians' offices, diagnostic imaging centers, and MCOs. Although approximately 80% of all radiologic technologists work full-time, part-time workers often are needed for some evening, weekend, or on-call hours.

Education: Most employers prefer formally trained radiologic technologists, and programs currently exist for radiography, radiation therapy, and diagnostic medical sonography. Radiography programs require a high school diploma for admission, and may be offered at the certificate, associate's degree, or bachelor's degree levels. In 1995, there were 692 accredited training programs ranging in length from one to four years at hospitals, vocational-technical institutes, colleges and universities, and the armed forces. The American Registry of Radiologic Technologists offers the ARRT certification for radiographers, the largest group of radiologic technologists. Licensing requirements vary from state to state.

Salary, Future Outlook: Full-time radiologic technologists earned an average of $28,800 in 1997. A technologists' income ranged from $24,596 to $36,244, depending on years of experience, the employer, and geographical location.

In 1996, radiologic technology contributed 174,000 workers to the U.S. workforce. While more technologists are likely to be employed over the next ten years, competition from a large pool of well-qualified applications is likely to be fierce. The wealth of advances in diagnostic imaging and a rise in the number of patients requiring these procedures will contribute to growth in the field. The high cost that goes along with many of these new technologies will, however, result in fewer job openings than one would expect. Physician offices and clinics will show the greatest employment increase for radiologic technologists.

Index: *American College of Radiology, American Society of Radiologic Technologists*

RESPIRATORY THERAPIST

Description: Registered respiratory therapists (RRTs) work under a physician's supervision to treat and care for patients with pulmonary disorders. Patients may sufferer from chronic asthma or emphysema, or may be victims of heart attack, stroke, shock, or AIDS. Respiratory therapists care for premature infants with underdeveloped lungs, as well as for the elderly who have increased susceptibility to pulmonary disease. Some common duties of a respiratory therapist include: administering oxygen to stimulate or compensate for breathing, measuring lung capacity, monitoring blood concentrations of oxygen, carbon dioxide, and pH level (acidity), and using equipment such as ventilators to maintain a patient's oxygen supply. Respiratory therapists may administer aerosol medications to patients for inhalation, or position patients in a way which prevents mucus buildup and lung obstruction. Recently, respiratory therapists have begun to assume the additional duties of cardiopulmonary technologists and may choose to specialize in other specific areas within the profession. Administrative or supervisory tasks may also be performed by respiratory therapists as they keep accurate patient records and supervise a team of respiratory personnel.

Close to 90% of respiratory therapists work in the respiratory care, anesthesiology, or pulmonary medicine departments of hospitals. Other career opportunities may exist in nursing homes, home health agencies, physicians' offices, or medical equipment rental companies. Most respiratory therapists work between 35-40 hours per week, and hospital employees may spend some of these hours in late night or weekend shifts.

Education: All entrants into the respiratory therapy field must complete a formal training program. The type of credential awarded and length of program varies among the 275 accredited programs for respiratory therapists.Community colleges offer two-year programs and award an associate's degree, while four-year colleges and universities award a bachelor's degree. If an individual has a bachelor's degree in a health related nonrespiratory field, he or she may complete a program of one to two years and spend two years in a clinical environment to be eligible for certification. The National Board for Respiratory Care conducts the certification examination and will award the RRT credential. Respiratory therapists with the most education and training will typically be given positions in critical rather than general care settings.

Salary, Future Outlook: Full-time respiratory therapists averaged $636 per week in 1996, or approximately $33,070 a year. For those therapists specifically in hospitals or medical centers, the average income was a comparable $32,500 in 1997. Therapists with advanced training or specialization may earn a larger salary, although the factors of employer, years in the field, and location all weigh into the salary determination.

Because the elderly are especially prone to lung disease and other disorders which complicate respiration, their rising numbers will increase the demand for respiratory therapy providers. As medical advances for premature infants and heart attack, stroke, and AIDS victims increase in the next ten years, more respiratory workers may be needed to administer new treatment options. Increased hiring will be most pronounced in home care and contract service agencies. In all settings, respiratory therapists skilled in specialized areas will be in the greatest demand.

Index: *American Association for Respiratory Care, Commission on Accreditation of Allied Health Education Programs*

RESPIRATORY THERAPY TECHNICIAN

Description: Certified respiratory therapy technicians (CRTTs) work with respiratory therapists to aid in the care of patients with lung or breathing disorders. They have less freedom and independence in working with patients directly, and may simply assist the respiratory therapist during actual treatment. Hospitals are the primary employer of respiratory therapy technicians, although other career opportunities exist in the same settings where respiratory therapists work.

Education: There are differences in the degree of training required for these two respiratory care workers. Technician programs generally last from a year to a year and a half, and award a certificate of completion. In 1996, there were 210 of these accredited programs. The National Board for Respiratory Care offers a certification examination for technicians which entitles successful parties to use the credential CRTT. Often, respiratory therapist technicians first take the technician certification exam, and complete two more years of clinical work to become eligible for the respiratory therapist certification exam.

Salary, Future Outlook: Technicians interested in earning the average $32,500 salary of a therapist should pursue further training, as it is unlikely that they will reach that pay level without it. As long as people suffer from respiratory ailments, the need for experienced respiratory care workers will be great, and as the health care industry scales down spending, the respiratory therapy technician may acquire more job responsibilities as they assume some of the duties of the higher-paid respiratory therapists.

Index: *American Association for Respiratory Care, Commission on Accreditation of Allied Health Education Programs*

SURGICAL TECHNOLOGIST

Description: Surgical technologists work as members of the surgical team to prepare the operating room for surgery, assist during surgery, and carry out the proper post-operative procedures. Technologists ensure that the operating room and all instruments are properly sterilized, ready the patient for surgery by preparing the incision site, transport the patient to the operating room, position them for surgery, and monitor the patient during and after the procedure. A *scrub technologist* assists the surgeons by handing them instruments during the surgery and ensures that the immediate surgical field remains sterile. A *circulating technologist* moves in and out of the sterile field, monitors supplies used during surgery, keeps accurate records of the surgical procedure, transfers and positions the patient for surgery, and sterilizes the patient's incision site. An *assisting technologist* has advanced training and is qualified to provide retraction at the incision site, sponge blood excesses, suction and irrigate as needed, assist in suturing the incision wound, and apply surgical dressings.

Surgical technologists are typically employed in hospital operating rooms but may also be stationed in delivery rooms, emergency rooms, and in central supply departments. Increasingly, technologists may be hired by clinics, outpatient surgical centers, physician or dental offices where minor surgery is performed, and in other facilities that require a sterile environment specialist. Most surgical technologists will work a 40-hour week, but may need to be available on weekends, in the evenings, and on holidays.

Education: In 1995, there were 147 accredited surgical technology training programs. Usually, a high school diploma is a prerequisite for admission to these programs, which may be offered by community and junior colleges, hospitals, and vocational-technical institutions. The length of training ranges from nine months to 24 months, depending on whether a certificate, diploma, or associate's degree is awarded. Voluntary certification is offered by the Liaison Council on Certification for Surgical Technologists which awards the CST designation — Certified Surgical Technologist.

Salary, Future Outlook: Earnings in this field vary by setting, the employer, and whether the surgical technologist is a scrub, assisting, or circulating type. In 1996, the median income for a full-time worker was $25,000 although salaries ranged from $20,900 to $28,000.

The job outlook for surgical technologists is likely to be great over the next ten years. New advances in the surgical field will make surgery a more popular method of medical treatment. The increase in the number of elderly in this country will account for a surplus of surgical candidates, and the trend toward outpatient surgery will mean that medical centers and physicians' offices will require surgical staffing. Often, surgical technologists are less expensive than operating room nurses. All of these factors will contribute to a steady demand for surgical technologists into the next century.

Index: *Association of Surgical Technologists, Commission on Accreditation of Allied Health Education Programs*

The most rewarding aspect of this work is making a difference in the lives of those with physical, mental, emotional, or social disabilities. With today's advances in medicine and health technology, trauma victims, premature infants, and the infirm are more likely to survive than previously. However, many will be handicapped and require the assistance of trained professionals to adjust to their disability and function on their own.

Speech-language pathologists help patients with communication problems master proper language and speech, while audiologists work with hearing-impaired individuals. *Physical therapists* and *athletic trainers* promote the physical health of patients recovering from injury or trauma. *Specialists for the visually disabled* help patients whose sight is irrevocably damaged learn skills which will help them function in their day-to-day activities. *Orthotists and prosthetists* also work with individuals suffering from a permanent disability, as they manufacture and fit artificial limbs to replace those that have been lost. *Rehabilitation counselors* have an active role in mainstreaming handicapped patients into a normal life of work and independent living.

Many specialists, such as *creative arts and activity therapists, occupational therapists*, and *recreational therapists*, teach patients skills which foster their productivity and usefulness, in spite of their disability. Assistants to these therapeutic and rehabilitative personnel, such as *occupational therapy assistants* and *physical therapy assistants*, are typically less expensive to hire than therapists themselves, and will experience significant job growth as administrators try to contain health care costs.

AUDIOLOGIST

Description: Audiologists are professionals specializing in the study of normal and impaired hearing, including the prevention of hearing loss, identification and assessment of hearing problems, and the rehabilitation of persons with hearing impairment. Daily duties include conducting ear examinations, training clients in speech and lip reading, measuring noise levels in work settings, and teaching individuals to use hearing aids or other helpful devices. An audiologist sees all types of hearing-impaired individuals—from children born with auditory abnormalities to elderly individuals just beginning to adjust to hearing loss. They frequently work with medical specialists, educators, engineers, scientists, and other health professionals in a variety of work settings.

An audiologist may work in a hospital, physician's office, or in a speech-language pathology/audiology clinic. They may also be hired by home health agencies to assist the elderly, or work in schools to help children with hearing problems. Some audiologists may choose private practice and open their own office, or contract their services to hospitals, schools, nursing homes, and industrial companies. The majority of audiologists are employed on a full-time basis and work close to 40 hours a week.

Education: To be a practicing audiologist requires at least a master's degree and, by the year 2005, a PhD may be mandatory for licensing. Additional requirements include a significant number of hours of clinical work, passing a national examination, and fulfilling a post-graduate requirement of experience in the field. Over 200 colleges and universities have audiology master's programs. The American Speech-Language-Hearing Association certifies competent individuals by awarding the Certificate of Clinical Competence (CCC), and certain states have an established licensing requirement for audiologists. A PhD is almost always needed for audiology positions in colleges, universities, and some hospitals.

Salary, Future Outlook: In 1997, certified audiologists with less than three years of experience reportedly earned an annual income of $32,000. Audiologists with significant experience in the field earned up to $55,000 a year. A doctoral degree will usually guarantee an even greater income, and the audiologist's geographic location will also make an appreciable difference in earning potential.

Due to changing population dynamics and advances in medical technology, the job outlook for audiologists is likely to be great over the next ten years. As the elderly population grows, so will the demand for hearing aids and other audiologic services. Advances in medicine and neonatology will account for a greater number of accident victims and disabled newborns who will need audiological assistance and rehabilitation. Schools will employ audiologists with increasing frequency to manage special education programs for students, and the number of private practice audiologists willing to contract out their services will increase.

Index: *American Health Care Association, American Speech-Language Hearing Association*

ATHLETIC TRAINER

Description: Athletic trainers prevent, care for, and rehabilitate athletic injuries, following treatment and rehabilitation procedures prescribed by the team physician. Trainers give immediate first aid, tape injuries, supervise diets, assist in purchasing and fitting athletic equipment, and educate athletes about good lifetime health habits. On game day, an athletic trainer may help prepare athletes for competition, recommend that certain players refrain from physical activity, and treat any injuries that may occur during the competition. *Kinesiology* is a closely related field of study that focuses on human movement and physical activity. Students with a background in kinesiology may seek positions in athletic training, coaching, physical fitness, medicine, and physical therapy.

Athletic trainers work for educational institutions with sports teams, professional team franchises, and sports medicine clinics. High schools, along with colleges and universities, may hire athletic trainers to monitor athletes from a wide range of sports teams. Professional football, baseball, hockey, and basketball teams almost always have a permanent athletic trainer on staff. Sports medicine clinics see individual athletes as patients, and may attend to older clientele as well. Other possible places for employment include businesses with athletic training facilities and health clubs. Trainers may work year-round and full-time with high school, college, and professional teams, or may work on a seasonal basis which varies by sport. Sports medicine clinics and health clubs hire athletic trainers on a permanent basis. Typical work hours will vary by employer. For some sports teams, extensive travel may be mandatory.

Education: Over 100 accredited institutions offer bachelor's and master's degrees in athletic training. The National Athletic Training Association (NATA) also has graduate level programs for those interested in furthering their education. Most employers require their athletic trainers to be certified; this involves graduation from an accredited program, fulfillment of internship hours (supervised training and additional coursework), and successful completion of the certification examination offered by the NATA Board of Certification. States have individualized licensing requirements.

Salary, Future Outlook: Sports medicine is a rapidly growing field, and each year a growing number of students aspire towards a career in athletic training. Although jobs with professional sports teams may be considered the most glamorous, these positions are limited. As physical fitness and exercise become more prevalent, a rise in the number of sports-related injuries will likely follow. Athletic trainers will be needed to teach proper health and exercise behaviors, and tend to the inevitable injuries that will occur. Sports medicine clinics will become increasingly popular, especially as new rehabilitative regimens and procedures are developed. In 1995, full-time athletic trainers earned a median salary of $28,550. Earnings will vary according to geographic location and work setting.

Index: *Commission on Accreditation of Allied Health Education Programs, National Athletic Trainers Association*

CREATIVE ARTS AND ACTIVITIES THERAPIST

Description: *Art therapists, dance therapists, horticultural therapists*, and *music therapists* devise programs that use their artistic talents and health skills to effect positive changes in the mental and physical well-being of people. Though they work primarily with the mentally and emotionally disturbed, mentally retarded, and physically or learning disabled, they may also work with healthy children and adults. Art therapists encourage a patient's artistic abilities and instill a sense of accomplishment. Dance therapists believe that movement creates physical and emotional release for patients. Horticultural therapists increase patients' psychological and social growth by assisting them in growing and caring for plants; often, working towards a tenable goal increases self-esteem and sense of responsibility. Music therapists use music as an emotional outlet, trigger for movement, and motivation for rehabilitation; by listening to, or even creating, music, patients may experience pain reduction and relaxation. These therapists may work on an individualized basis with patients, or hold large group sessions in rehabilitative institutions.

Art, dance, horticultural, and music therapists may work in hospitals, nursing homes, mental health rehabilitation facilities, or centers for the learning or developmentally disabled. Substance abuse clinics and correctional facilities may also seek therapists to run creativity and activity programs. Therapists may be hired by individual families or may conduct research in their respective fields. Typically, full-time therapists work a standard 40-hour work week. Some may choose to engage in art, dance, horticultural, and music therapy on a part-time basis as a career extension.

Education: Often, the training required includes courses in psychology or behavioral sciences, in addition to art, dance, horticulture, or music training. For entrance into the *art therapy* field, a bachelor's degree is mandatory and a master's is necessary to practice professionally. There are over 100 undergraduate and graduate training programs accredited by the American Art Therapy Association, which also certifies qualified individuals as an Art Therapist, Registered (ATR). *Dance therapists* must also have a master's degree to practice, and there are currently fewer than ten institutions offering this graduate-level training. The American Dance Therapy Association awards two levels of certification: Dance Therapist, Registered (DTR) and Academy of Dance Therapists, Registered (ADTR) to those who have completed additional clinical work. To become a *horticultural therapist* requires a bachelor's degree in horticulture, at minimum. The American Horticultural Therapy Association also offers two levels of certification: Horticultural Therapist, Registered (HTR) and Horticulture Therapist Master (HTM) for those with advanced education and training. *Music therapists* also must have their bachelor's degree and complete a six-month clinical internship in the field. The National Association for Music Therapy conducts a certification exam and registers music therapists with the initials Registered Music Therapist (RMT).

Salary, Future Outlook: For creative arts and activities therapists, individual salary will vary widely by subject specialization, geographic location, years of experience, and degree earned. While some therapists may start at as little as $20,000, there are opportunities to increase this income to as much as $50,000. Therapists in advanced research or teaching positions may earn even more.

Over the next ten years, art, dance, music, and horticultural therapy will provide an increasing number of individuals with careers in health care. As an alternative to standard medication treatments, these therapies will appeal to those wishing to try a less invasive and more creative method of rehabilitation. As the population ages, the number of elderly individuals needing rehabilitative therapy will also increase. Therapy regimens in art, dance, music, and horticulture are expected to have a special appeal to these patients, who often will develop lifelong hobbies.

Index: *American Art Therapy Association, American Dance Therapy, American Music Therapy Association, American Horticultural Therapy Association*

OCCUPATIONAL THERAPIST

Description: Occupational therapists (OTs) help disabled people of all ages learn or regain the skills they need to live independent, productive, and satisfying lives. Therapists may help someone who is physically disabled learn daily living skills, such as dressing, cooking, or using transportation. They may work with children with developmental or learning disabilities by helping parents and teachers to provide skills these children need to learn and grow. Occupational therapists assist people with emotional disabilities and mental illness to learn to cope with the demands of daily living and to plan and structure work and leisure time. Specifically, an occupational therapist may lead the patient in physical exercise, assist the patient in operating rehabilitative equipment and computer programs, work in the classroom to assimilate disabled children into school settings, and teach finance, time management, and social survival skills to the mentally handicapped. *Industrial therapists* are occupational therapists who arrange for their patients to hold jobs and monitor their activities and progress. All therapists must keep accurate records of their patients' histories and specific visits, and may be called upon to consult with other health providers in forming treatment plans.

Hospitals, including large rehabilitative and mental health facilities, employ the greatest number of occupational therapists. Public schools and schools for the learning disabled also provide jobs for a large portion of practicing therapists. Some other settings include nursing homes, mental health clinics, and specialized occupational therapy offices. While few occupational therapists are self-employed, the number in solo or group practice may soon increase. Often, these therapists may serve larger institutions or individual families on a contractual basis. A standard work schedule is the 40-hour business week, yet some occupational therapists, especially those under contract, may work during the evening or on weekends.

Education: The minimum educational requirement for entry into the occupational therapy field is a bachelor's degree. There are approximately 70 bachelor's degree programs and 20 master's degree programs. Those interested in obtaining the title of Registered Occupational Therapist must complete an accredited graduate level program, and pass an examination of the American Occupational Therapy Certification Board. For those with a bachelor's degree in a field other than occupational therapy, a certificate program will provide the necessary training needed to sit for the certification examination. Approximately ten such certification programs exist. Students also complete a supervised internship which provides them with hands-on experience and a chance to gain exposure to daily job tasks.

Salary, Future Outlook: For full-time occupational therapists, the average annual salary was $42,700 in 1997. Actual salaries may be higher, depending on years of experience, state of employment, and work setting. Therapists employed in private practice generally earn more than those who are salaried.

In 1996, there were 57,000 occupational therapists employed in the work force. The job outlook for occupational therapists will be excellent in the next ten years. With advances in medical technology, the survival rate for critically injured individuals has greatly improved, and these patients will need occupational therapy. As more and more disabled children are mainstreamed into public schools, occupational therapists will be called upon to aid in this transition. Hospitals will continue to employ the largest number of therapists, but their services will also be in demand in home health agencies. With changes in current legislation, more occupational therapists will move to private practice because they are now able to charge Medicare for services provided.

Index: *American Health Care Association, The American Occupational Therapy Association*

OCCUPATIONAL THERAPY ASSISTANT

Description: Occupational therapy assistants (OTA) work with patients to complete the treatment regimen set up by occupational therapists. They monitor the patient's progress and make explicit notes for a report to the therapist. An assistant may recommend changes in treatment or alter the treatment upon the therapist's orders to do so. On a typical day, an occupational therapy assistant may teach a disabled patient how to get around despite limited mobility, perform routine strengthening or muscle toning exercises with the patient, or simply carry out office tasks, such as managing insurance forms and other paperwork.

Approximately 30% of occupational therapy assistants are employed by hospitals. Over 25% worked in nursing and personal care facilities. The remainder were employed in the offices of occupational therapists, home care agencies, and offices of other health care workers. A typical work week is 40 hours in length, and some clients prefer evening and weekend appointments.

Education: An associate's degree from an accredited training program is usually required for an occupational therapy assistant. There are approximately 80 such programs offered by community colleges and technical schools, usually lasting for two years. Often, applicants with prior experience in the health field or with an educational background in the sciences will be more readily accepted in these programs. Licensing requirements vary from state to state. Many of the occupational therapy assistant's daily tasks are learned and perfected on the job.

Salary, Future Outlook: An occupational therapy assistant's earnings will vary by employer, state of employment, and extent of job responsibility. In 1995, the average income was reportedly $27,442.

In 1996, 16,000 occupational therapy assistant were licensed and practicing. Despite the small size of the field, assistants are likely to have a good job outlook over the next ten years, due to the success of the occupational therapy field. As baby boomers reach later life, and the number of individuals requiring therapeutic services increases, all occupational therapy workers will be in demand. Because their services are not as expensive, assistants will be hired to perform some tasks that used to be left to occupational therapists.

Index: *American Health Care Association, The American Occupational Therapy Association*

PHYSICAL THERAPIST

Description: Physical therapists (PTs) work with people who have been physically disabled by illness or accident, or who are born with a handicap. Treatment may include exercise to improve muscle strength and coordination, applying heat, cold, water, or electricity to relieve pain or to change the patient's condition, therapeutic massages to relieve pain and reduce swelling, and the use of wheelchairs or crutches to restore a patient's mobility. Physical therapists work with individuals suffering from a wide range of conditions, including multiple sclerosis and cerebral palsy, burn injuries, nerve damage, amputation, or cardiovascular disease and arthritis. A physical therapist reviews a patient's medical history, consults with his or her physician, and decides upon a treatment plan complete with timeline and the desired end result.

While 30% of practicing physical therapists were employed by hospitals in 1995, 25% worked in specialized physical therapy offices. Others worked in physicians' offices, nursing homes, schools, or rehabilitation centers. Increasingly, therapists may opt to work in their own private practice and may contract their services to rehabilitative health centers or individual patients. Advanced physical therapists may engage in research in the field, or teach at academic institutions. A 40-hour work week with some evening or weekend hours is standard for most physical therapists.

Education: Employment in the field of physical therapy requires a training program accredited by the American Physical Therapy Association. All physical therapists must also be licensed by the state in which they choose to practice. In 1995, there were 65 bachelor's degree programs and 80 master's degree programs, with more being developed. These programs are very selective and admission is competitive. Firsthand experience and high grades in the sciences will give an applicant the edge over the rest of the field. Those with a bachelor's degree in a related science are still eligible for entrance into a master's degree program. A master's degree in physical therapy is almost always required for advanced administrative or other upper level jobs.

Salary, Future Outlook: Full-time physical therapists earned an average of $757 per week, or approximately $39,360 a year, in 1996. Those employed exclusively in hospitals and medical centers earned $48,000 that same year. Often, physical therapists with a private practice had a greater earning potential than those who were salaried. As in any career, earnings depend on the employer, location, and extent of training or education.

Although the number of practicing physical therapists has increased drastically over the last few years, sufficient demand for their services still exists. There were 115,000 therapists in 1996 and more are expected to enter the work force over the next ten years. Advances in medical technology will mean that more trauma victims and premature infants will survive and require rehabilitative services. Physical therapists will acquire more elderly patients with chronic conditions and encounter more victims of heart attack and stroke. As the country becomes more health conscious, the physical therapist will counsel patients on safer exercise techniques and encourage safety in the workplace.

Index: *American Health Care Association, American Physical Therapy Association*

PHYSICAL THERAPY ASSISTANT

Description: Physical therapy assistants (PTAs) perform routine treatment procedures as directed by physical therapists and assist them with more complex procedures. An assistant may monitor a patient's progress on exercise equipment, perform massage, heat/cold, electrical and ultrasound therapy, and provide the therapist with a detailed account of all therapeutic sessions. Clerical tasks, supply maintenance, and paperwork are often included among the duties of a physical therapist assistant, but the extent of these assignments will vary from setting to setting.

More than 50% of all physical therapy assistants work either in a hospital or in a physical therapy office. Other common places of employment include nursing homes, physicians' offices, sports medicine clinics, and any other setting where one may find a physical therapist. Close to 80% of all physical therapy assistant are full time salaried workers, and they are often needed to staff offices and clinics over the weekend and during some evenings.

Education: The standard degree requirement for a physical therapy assistant is an associate's degree that may be obtained from a community or junior college. As of 1995, there were well over 200 accredited programs in the United States. Although there are numerous training programs, each has a limited number of openings, and competition for admission is fierce. Most programs last two years, and state laws mandate whether or not all graduates must seek licensure. Typically, assistants must at least acquire CPR and first aid certification, and must fulfill the required number of hours of clinical experience.

Salary, Future Outlook: Recent salary data sets the median annual income for physical therapy assistants at $24,000. Often, those employed in private physical therapy offices surpass this sum, and others with more extensive training and experience may also see an increased salary.

For all workers in the field of physical therapy, the future is promising. Physical therapy assistants filled 84,000 openings in 1996, and their numbers are expected to rise over the next ten years. As the baby boomer generation ages, they will frequent physical therapy offices for rehabilitation of chronic conditions as well as heart attacks and strokes. Increasingly, assistants will assume some of the duties that were once performed exclusively by physical therapists.

Index: *American Health Care Association, American Physical Therapy Association*

ORTHOTIST AND PROSTHETIST

Description: Certified orthotists (COs) and certified prosthetists (CPs) fabricate and fit upper and lower limb devices designed to replace or repair those lost or disabled through injury or disease. Orthotists fabricate and fit orthopedic braces; prosthetists fabricate and fit artificial limbs. Some persons may be qualified to work in both areas. They examine and measure patients and custom fabricate prosthetic or orthotic devices to individual specifications. These workers must be familiar with different materials and designs, accurately measure the static and dynamic proportions of the affected limb, and keep accurate patient record to assure that they follow a physician's exact directive. Orthotists and prosthetists supervise and are assisted by *Orthotic/Prosthetic Technicians.* Technicians make and repair the devices but do not have patient contact.

Orthotists and prosthetists work in a variety of health settings. Often, these practitioners may have their own private practice, or work in another privately owned facility. Hospitals, laboratories, and even government agencies also employ orthotists and prosthetists. For most workers, a typical work week lasts 40 hours and consists of nine-to-five days. Those orthotists and prosthetists who are self-employed or work in practices must be flexible to accommodate patients' schedules and may work some evening or weekend hours. Technicians will typically work a standard 40-hour business week.

Education: In order to practice as an orthotist or prosthetist, an individual must be certified by the American Board for Certification in Orthotics and Prosthetics, Inc. The prerequisites to certification include a bachelor's degree, specific training courses in orthotics and prosthetics, and at least one year of supervised experience in the field. There are only a few accredited training programs in the United States, and they award either a bachelor's degree or postbaccalaureate certificate. Upon completing training and passing the certification examination, one may use the credentials of CO, CP or Certified Prosthetist/Orthotist (CPO). The American Board of Certification also is responsible for awarding the title of Registered Technician to those who have had the appropriate education (usually a certificate training program) or experience (at least two years in a clinical setting).

Salary, Future Outlook: As medical and technological advances in the field of orthotics and prosthetics continue, the demand for skilled and experienced workers will be great. Medical innovations are allowing more and more trauma victims and handicapped infants to survive and become prime candidates for orthotic or prosthetic care. Society is more accepting of individuals with artificial limbs and braces, and the number of patients requesting them will grow. Orthotists and prosthetists are now receiving due recognition for helping disabled individuals lead normal and productive lives.

Index: *American Board for Certification in Orthotics and Prosthetics, Inc., Commission on Accreditation of Allied Health Education Programs*

RECREATIONAL THERAPIST

Description: Recreational therapists, also known as therapeutic recreation specialists, work with individuals with physical, social, or emotional disabilities. Through recreation activities, the therapist assists in eliminating barriers to leisure and developing leisure skills. This may mean enabling a handicapped individual to access a public recreational facility, helping a shy patient socialize with peers, or exposing an individual to a new and exciting experience. Some typical recreational activities may include field trips to sporting events, sightseeing excursions, picnics, outdoor activities and games, arts and crafts, and music. Recreational therapists may work solely with the elderly, with those afflicted with a particular medical malady, or as part of a community-wide program that includes a broad range of individuals.

Although work settings may vary, a recreational therapist will typically work a 40-hour week. Common places of employment include hospitals and nursing homes, which employed 50% and 33%, of all therapists in 1994. Other sites include community mental health centers, correctional facilities, adult care programs, and substance abuse centers. Another option is self-employment, which allows a therapist to contract services to large facilities or individual families.

Education: There are more than 150 training programs in recreational therapy and about half of them are accredited. These programs offered varied degrees including associate's, bachelor's, master's, and doctoral. While an associate's degree may suffice for some nursing home or community positions, hospitals and larger clinical facilities generally require at least a bachelor's degree. Additionally, those individuals seeking certification will need to complete 360 hours of supervised work experience. The certification examination is conducted by the National Council for Therapeutic Recreation Certification, and a passing score denotes a mastery of the skills necessary to succeed in the field.

Salary, Future Outlook: In 1996, the median income for all recreational therapists was $33,000. Those employed by the government earned up to $39,400 annually in 1997. Therapists in private practice, in a supervisory position, or having more education and experience will typically surpass this median value. Employer and geographic location may also factor into actual income.

The employment outlook for recreational therapists is likely to be good over the next ten years. These therapists held over 31,000 jobs and that number continues to rise today. Hospitals will consistently employ the majority of recreation therapists to supervise outpatient and adult day care programs. As the baby boomer generation reaches a later stage in life, the demand for therapists to staff nursing homes and retirement community programs will also rise. Employment prospects will be best for those recreational therapists with experience in a clinical setting.

Index: *American Therapeutic Recreation Association*

REHABILITATION COUNSELOR

Description: Rehabilitation counselors help people with physical, mental, or social disabilities return to a satisfying and productive life. These counselors use work as a method of assisting the disabled to fulfill their full potential. They may counsel them about job opportunities and training availability, assist in job placement, or provide counseling to help the person adjust successfully to the new work situation. A rehabilitation counselor also helps disabled individuals adjust to their limitations, assesses an individual's potential to live independently, and confers often with a patient's family, physician, social worker, occupational therapist, and psychologist.

There are an unlimited number of work settings for rehabilitation counselors. State and federal agencies commonly hire these counselors, as do schools, substance abuse rehabilitation programs, mental health clinics, independent living centers, group homes, nursing homes, insurance companies, and correctional centers. Employers from all fields utilize a rehabilitation counselor's knowledge of the legal issues involved in employing a disabled individual and may hire them on as full-time staff. Counselors typically work a standard 40-hour week; those that are self-employed may work extended hours.

Education: Students interested in rehabilitation counseling usually obtain a bachelor's degree in a related field, and then enroll in a two year master's program. The clinical training that is a part of most master's programs includes 600 hours of supervised clinical experience. There are currently more than 80 accredited training programs in rehabilitation counselor education. The Commission on Rehabilitation Counselor Certification certifies counselors who have fulfilled their requirements, and licensure may be pursued directly through the state of employment.

Salary, Future Outlook: In 1996, the median annual salary for rehabilitation counselors was $35,800. Generally, counselors with a private practice or those who work for large private firms will earn substantially more. Earning potential will also vary by years of experience, work setting, and level or education.

The demand for rehabilitation counselors is likely to be great in the near future. The percentage of the U.S. population with some form of disability is astounding, and the number of rehabilitation counselors trained to help them is alarmingly small. As insurance companies begin to pay for the services rendered by rehabilitation counselors, equal employment legislation becomes enforced in almost all workplaces, and the elderly population grows, experienced counselors will find no shortage of job opportunities.

Index: *National Rehabilitation Counseling Association*

SPECIALIST FOR THE VISUALLY DISABLED

Description: Specialists for the visually disabled work in a number of areas with children and adults who are blind or partially sighted. *Orientation and mobility instructors* teach persons how to travel independently indoors and outdoors in familiar and unfamiliar surroundings. *Rehabilitation teachers* work primarily with adults or newly blinded individuals teaching them skills needed to live and work more independently. They instruct in communication skills such as Braille, personal or home management skills such as hygiene or cooking, and leisure skills, such as handicrafts and hobbies. *Special educators of children* work with elementary and secondary students in public, private, or residential schools. They teach students communication skills, assist with regular studies and technological adaptations, or help facilitate the production of their lessons in an appropriate medium like Braille, large print, or audio tape. Some teachers also specialize in working with children who have multiple handicaps or are deaf-blind.

Many specialists for the visually disabled are employed in the public educational system. Private schools for the visually impaired, an individual's home, or special residential facilities are also common work settings. Orientation and mobility instructors may spend much time outdoors or in public facilities as they teach those with sight problems how to maneuver. Specialists may work a standard business day or customize their work schedule to an individual patient or institution.

Education: Educational requirements for a specialist for the visually disabled will vary, depending on the work setting. Many institutions offer a bachelor's degree in this area, although it is still possible to enter a master's program with a degree in a different field. States may have individualized certification and licensing requirements for certain positions. The most practical and useful training, however, is actual hands-on experience with visually impaired individuals. If a family member is visually impaired or a student has volunteered extensively in a program for the visually impaired, these experiences will best suit the individual for a career in the field.

Salary, Future Outlook: Like other special educators, specialists for the visually disabled earned close to $36,900 in 1995. Most often, workers in this salary range had a master's degree, and have been in the field for a number of years. Place of employment greatly affects one's salary, as private institutions characteristically pay higher wages.

Future employment prospects for specialists for the visually disabled are likely to be good. As more and more visually impaired children are mainstreamed into public school classrooms, special educators will be needed to facilitate their transition. As the population of elderly individuals rises, so will the number of people with partial or total loss of sight. Rehabilitation teachers and orientation and mobility instructors will be increasingly sought out to provide their critical services.

Index: *Association for Education and Rehabilitation of the Blind and Visually Impaired*

SPEECH-LANGUAGE PATHOLOGIST

Description: Speech-language pathologists are professionals concerned with the research, evaluation, and treatment of human communication problems. They work with people of all ages and types of symptoms, including stuttering, harsh voice, inappropriate pitch, and eating or swallowing difficulties. Their patients may also have problems producing and understanding language. Causes of such speech problems can date back to birth and include mental retardation, cerebral palsy, and cleft palate. Other causes striking later in life may be hearing loss, brain injury, or stroke. For all patients, the speech-language pathologist determines the exact nature of the disability and decides upon an adequate treatment regimen.

Speech-language pathologists are employed in a variety of work settings including schools, hospitals, speech-language pathology and audiology offices, nursing homes, and rehabilitation centers. Others may choose to enter private solo or group practice and collect their own group of clients. A typical working day lasts from nine to five, and full-time workers outnumber those employed part time.

Education: To be a practicing speech-language pathologist, generally requires a master's degree from an institution accredited by the American Speech-Language-Hearing Association. There are currently close to 200 such institutions. Those with a bachelor's degree in Speech Language Pathology or communications may work in some schools, but a master's is needed for most positions. The American Speech-Language-Hearing Association awards the Certificate of Clinical Competence (CCC) to all pathologists who have their master's, 300-375 hours of clinical experience and a nine month post-graduate internship.

Salary, Future Outlook: Speech-language pathologists just starting their career earned an average of $38,000 annually in 1997. Those in practice for over 22 years were earning up to $52,000 in that same year. Generally, income will vary by geographic location, work setting, and level of education completed.

The employment outlook for speech-language pathologists is expected to be excellent over the next ten years, especially in schools. As more school systems push for mandatory screening and early detection, more speech disorders will be diagnosed. More victims of brain injury and stroke will be likely to survive due to advances in medical technology, and their resultant speech abnormalities will need treatment. The elderly, who have a disproportionate number of speech and communication problems, will grow in number and justify the increased hiring of more speech-language pathology professionals.

Index: *American Health Care Association, American Speech-Language Hearing Association*

Mean Salary for Speech-Language Pathologist and Audiologists by Year, 1993-1997

	Speech-language pathologists	Audiologists
1993	$36,000	$38,450
1995	$39,950	$40,122
1997	$44,000	$43,000

Source: American Speech-Language Hearing Association, 1997 Edition Salary Report

VETERINARY MEDICINE

For many households, the pet is a family member whose health just is as important as their own. Owners are willing to spend the money necessary to ensure that their pet receives proper preve' .ve veterinary care and medical treatment. Veterinary professionals are not only animal lovers, but trained medical and technical specialists who care for animals of all types and sizes.

The *veterinarian* is the primary animal health care provider who treats diseased animals, counsels owners on proper pet nutrition and maintenance and prescribes vaccines and other preventive medications. While one typically thinks of a veterinarian as treating dogs and cats in a private practice, they also are involved in wildlife preservation, agriculture, and medical research which benefits human health. *Veterinary technicians* and *veterinary assistants* are crucial to the daily functioning of a veterinary practice, as they assist the veterinarian in all duties.

For bright and intelligent individuals willing to treat animals in sickness and in health, a career in veterinary medicine is likely to be a rewarding choice.

Number and Percentage of Veterinarians by Practice Type and Employer, 1995

PRIVATE CLINICAL PRACTICE		
Large animal exclusive	1,805	(4.5%)
Large animal predominant	4,078	(10.1%)
Mixed animal	3,148	(7.8%)
Small animal predominant	5,376	(13.3%)
Small animal exclusive	22,839	(56.6%)
Equine	1,653	(4.1%)
Other	1,425	(3.5%)
PUBLIC AND CORPORATE EMPLOYMENT		
College or university	4,331	(45.8%)
Federal government	1,214	(12.8%)
State or local government	701	(7.4%)
Uniformed services	502	(5.3%)
Industrial	1,456	(15.4%)
Other	1,260	(13.3%)
GRAND TOTAL	54,852	

Source: American Veterinary Medical Association, Veterinary Economic Statistics 1995

VETERINARIAN

Description: Doctors of Veterinary Medicine (DVMs) not only provide care for animals, but also play a role in human disease prevention and public health. Generally, veterinarians diagnose, treat, and prevent illness or disease in animals via medication, surgery, or vaccination. Some veterinarians treat small animals such as household pets, while others may specialize in larger farm animals and livestock. Many vets are general practitioners, but specialty areas also exist: dentistry, dermatology, microbiology, surgery, zoological medicine, animal behavior, to name a few. Those DVMs in the area of human health may serve as food inspectors, researchers, epidemiologists, or livestock inspectors. They help assure that diseases are not spread from animal to human populations.

Veterinarians with small practices work out of private offices, clinics and animal hospitals. Large practitioners often travel to their patients on farms, ranches or even in zoos. Privately owned and group practices are common with small and large animal specialists, and over 30% of veterinarians are self-employed. The federal government is a primary employer of many veterinarians — especially within the Departments of Agriculture, Defense, and Health and Human Services. Other opportunities may exist in veterinary medical colleges, research and pharmaceutical companies, and zoos. It is not uncommon for veterinarians to work 40-50 hours a week, especially those trying to get established in private practice.

Education: To practice in almost every setting, veterinarians must have a DVM degree and a valid license. There are less than 30 colleges of veterinary medicine in the United States, and competition for admission is fierce. Most students complete a pre-veterinary curriculum as undergraduates, and gain hands-on experience working with animals in their free time. Either the GRE, MCAT, or Veterinary Aptitude Test are required for admission into a veterinary school. Veterinary programs last four years and state requirements for licensure vary. Specialization will require an additional three years of residency study.

Salary, Future Outlook: In 1995, starting veterinarians earned an income of $29,900. For all veterinarians in private practice, the average was $57,500. The location of a private practice is an important factor in salary determination, as is type of practice, and number of years in existence. For salaried governmental veterinarians, earnings averaged $57,600 in 1997.

Over the next ten years, the job prospects for veterinarians are likely to remain stable. In 1996, veterinarians held over 58,000 jobs and more will be needed in specialty areas, facilities practicing new breeding technology, and in disease control programs. The pet population, expected to multiply rapidly every year, will grow to include a new generation of family pets and stray animals that will require veterinary care.

Index: *American Veterinary Medical Association*

VETERINARY TECHNICIAN AND ASSISTANTS

Description: Veterinary technicians, sometimes referred to as technologists, work under the tutelage of practicing veterinarians and perform a wide range of duties. They work in the laboratory to conduct tests on animal specimens and prepare vaccines or tissue samples. Technicians may draw blood and prepare animals for surgery. Additionally, "vet techs" interact with the patient's owner and veterinarians to assist in the diagnosis and prevention of illness and disease. Veterinary assistants, also known as animal attendants and animal health assistants, perform duties similar to a veterinary technician but are trained on the job, as opposed to completing an accredited training program.

Often, veterinary technicians and assistants work in places where veterinarians are also found. Private veterinary practices, animal hospitals, research companies, public health agencies, food inspection facilities, and animal laboratories hire technicians to perform laboratory work and ease the burden of veterinarians. While some job openings may be full-time, part-time workers may be preferred by the employer.

Education: To qualify as a veterinary technician, one must earn an associate's degree from an American Veterinary Medical Association accredited program. Usually two years in length, these college level programs cover fundamentals of animal science and provide practical information and experience. Registration or certification for technicians is required by some states, and examinations are conducted by the Laboratory Animal Technician Certification Board. Assistants may not be required to have any formal schooling or training and will acquire basic job skills on the job.

Salary, Future Outlook: According to 1996 data, the typical veterinary technician and assistant earned on average salary $17,100. The type of employer, geographical location, and job performance all factor into the salary.

In 1996, there were about 33,000 veterinary assistants. Over the next ten years, growth of these jobs will parallel the trends in national job growth. As animal hospitals and government agencies adopt cost-cutting strategies, technicians and assistants will be accepting responsibilities that were once given only to licensed veterinarians. As long as veterinary services remain in demand in this country, technicians and assistants will provide the backbone for these services.

Index: *American Veterinary Medical Association*

In the past, most individuals paid little attention to their vision until it started to falter. Today, parents send their young children for vision screening and patients of all ages visit their vision care provider for annual preventive check-ups.

Optometrists are trained to test visual acuity, prescribe corrective eye wear and diagnose disease states of the eye. They are assisted by *paraoptometrists*, optometric assistants and technicians who are trained to perform key duties in the optometric practice. For those without serious vision problems, an annual visit to their optometrist is often adequate. An *ophthalmologist*, often assisted by *ophthalmic medical personnel*, treats surgical candidates and patients with advanced diseases of the eye. An *orthoptist* is another specialized vision care provider who treats children having crossed eyes and focusing problems. The *dispensing optician* is a professional with whom all eyeglass wearers are familiar. They not only sell eyeglasses, they also help manufacture lenses in accordance to a doctor's prescription, and may service contact lens wearers as well. A vision care provider is a respected health care professional.

As more elderly patients seek treatment for failing vision and the need for corrective eye wear grows, these careers will be excellent options for anyone seeking to enter the health care field.

DISPENSING OPTICIAN

Description: Dispensing opticians make and fit the eye glasses or lenses prescribed by *ophthalmologists* and **optometrists**. They measure facial contours and assist in frame and lens selection. Some opticians may also grind and create the lenses to proper magnification, but generally rely on assistant personnel to do this. Finally, dispensing opticians adjust and fit the frame to the customer's specifications and make any necessary repairs to broken frames or lenses. Some dispensing opticians specialize in fitting contact lenses, artificial eyes, or cosmetic shells to cover eye abnormalities. The techniques needed for these procedures often involve the use of specialized equipment and require additional precision for working so close to the delicate structures of the eye. Dispensing opticians must also assume the daily tasks of keeping and updating client records, maintaining stock and office supplies, and handling payments.

Opticians are generally employed in one of two places. A large portion are hired by ophthalmologists and optometrists who provide patients with the option to buy glasses directly. Other common work places are in privately owned stores and chain stores that sell eyeglasses. Some may work for large-scale eyeglass manufacturers, drug stores, or department stores. The typical optician works a full-time 40-hour week but must be accommodating to clients by working weekend or evening hours. Part-time employment is another viable option.

Education: Depending on the employer, training in this field may be done informally on the job, as part of a formal apprenticeship, or in a post-secondary institution. Generally, a small practice in opticianry will train employees on the job, while larger practices have a structured apprenticeship program which may last from two to four years. Formal training programs may be offered in community colleges and some universities and in 1995 there were close to 40 such programs. Programs can be one or two years in length, and a two-year program will award an associate's. State regulations concerning the licensing of opticians vary, and in many states, licensing is not required. The American Board of Opticianry and the National Contact Lens Examiners are two certifying bodies which allow dispensing opticians to voluntarily validate their professional status.

Salary, Future Outlook: Full-time dispensing opticians earned an average of $27,432 in 1997, and those in managerial positions earned even more. Optician who own their own stores may earn a larger salary, and earnings also vary by experience level and degree of training.

Over the next ten years, employment opportunities in the field of opticianry are expected to grow. In 1996, there were 67,000 dispensing opticians in the work force. As the number of middle-aged and elderly individuals grows, more people will need prescription eyewear to supplement failing eyesight. Additionally, as fashion tastes change, old glasses will need to be replaced with newer lenses and frames equipped with modern features. As with many other businesses, optical stores will increase employment when the market is good and dismiss employees during tougher financial times.

Index: *Opticians Association of America, Prevent Blindness America*

OPHTHALMIC MEDICAL PERSONNEL

Description: *Ophthalmic assistants, ophthalmic technicians,* and *ophthalmic technologists* assist the medical doctors who specialize in eye care (*Ophthalmologists*). Assistants perform routine procedures such as vision testing, obtaining patient histories, changing eye dressings, and administering eye medications. Technicians perform more advanced technical procedures, such as taking optical measurements or external ophthalmic photographs and providing limited assistance to the ophthalmologist during surgery. Ophthalmic technologists are the most highly trained ophthalmic medical personnel. They perform procedures requiring advanced technical skill and theoretical knowledge and must be familiar with sophisticated instruments and surgical procedures.

Most ophthalmic medical personnel are employed in hospitals, medical centers, and offices of ophthalmologists. Some may be employed in research laboratories or in the armed forces. Typically, assistants, technicians and technologists work a standard 40-hour work week and may put in overtime or extended hours as needed.

Education: There are over 34 existing training programs for the three levels of ophthalmic personnel taught at colleges, universities, and hospitals. These programs may offer training at the assistant, technician, or technologist level. They range in length from a few weeks to up to two years for technologists. The Joint Commission on Allied Health Personnel in Ophthalmology (JCAHPO) is the certifying body for ophthalmic medical personnel and awards the certification of Certified Ophthalmic Assistant (COA), Certified Ophthalmic Technician (COT) and Certified Ophthalmic Medical Technologist (COMT). Generally, certification eligibility is fulfilled by those who have completed an accredited training program and have had some clinical experience in the field. The JCAHPO also conducts certification examinations for the two subspecialties: ophthalmic surgical assisting and assisting in low vision.

Salary, Future Outlook: Salaries in this field vary by certification status, experience level, and employer. Generally, technologists earn the most money and assistants the least due to their differences in skill level and training. In 1995, technicians working full-time averaged close to $20,000 in income. Assistants and technologists earned salaries below and above this value respectively.

As with other workers in the eye care field, opthalmic medical personnel are likely to experience good job prospects in the future. As the baby boomer generation ages, the need for vision care will skyrocket. Increasingly, the public is becoming more concerned with proper optical health and visits to the ophthalmologists are more frequent. Experienced ophthalmic assistants at all three levels will be needed to manage an increased patient load and assume more of the tasks once performed by higher paid eye care personnel.

Index: *Commission on Accreditation of Allied Health Education Programs, Joint Commission on Allied Health Personnel in Ophthalmology, Prevent Blindness America*

OPTOMETRIST

Description: Optometrists, or doctors of optometry (ODs) independent primary health care providers who specialize in the examination, diagnosis, treatment, and management of diseases and disorders of the visual system. They treat the eye and its associated structures, as well as diagnosing related systemic conditions. As health care professionals, optometrists regularly identify signs of disease of both the eye and of the body and work with other health professionals in co-managing the care of patients. Doctors of optometry provide vision care by prescribing ophthalmic lenses, contact lenses, other optical aides, and vision therapy as indicated. They are authorized to use drugs in the diagnosis of eye problems or diseases in all 50 states, and may use drugs to treat eye disease in 46 states. Private practitioners must also assume the administrative and clerical duties of running a business.

The majority of optometrists work in private group or solo practices. They may also be employed by other optometrists or ophthalmologists, hospitals, HMOs or optical stores. ODs work at least 40-hour weeks, with many working up to 50 hours, including nights and weekends.

Education: To earn the title of doctor of optometry, one must complete a four year program at an accredited school of optometry. These schools require applicants to have completed at least three years of undergraduate training in addition to taking the Optometry Admissions Test (OAT). Competition for the limited spaces in these programs is fierce, and a good academic background is key. Individual states conduct their own written and clinical examinations for optometric licensing. Graduates may seek one year of advanced study to specialize in family practice optometry, pediatric optometry, geriatric optometry, vision therapy, contact lenses, hospital based optometry, primary care optometry, or ocular disease. Those wishing research or teaching positions may enter master's or PhD programs which emphasize visual health.

Salary, Future Outlook: In 1996, optometrists recently graduated from optometry school earned approximately $57,500. The average salary for optometrists was closer to $80,000. Often, doctors who specialize, have a private practice, or work in a higher income area will experience an increased earning potential.

There are many factors which will contribute to the demand for optometrists in this country. The number of middle aged individuals will rise and it is at this time that many will first need corrective vision care. As the elderly population rises, optometrists will have to handle more cases of cataracts, glaucoma, and other diseases common to people of this age group. In 1996, optometrist held about 41,000 jobs and that number is likely to remain pretty stable over the next ten years. Established practices are likely to expand to meet the patients' needs, and more assistant personnel will be hired to handle the increased work load.

Index: *American Optometric Association, Association of Schools and Colleges of Optometry, National Optometric Association, Prevent Blindness America*

PARAOPTOMETRISTS

Description: The title of paraoptometrist includes the *registered optometric assistants* (OptAR) and *registered optometric technicians* (OptTR) who assist optometrists. Assistants perform office and routine patient duties. They keep records, act as receptionists, assist patients with frame selection, and order prescribed lenses. While technicians may also be responsible for office tasks, they assist the optometrist in those activities that require more skills such as vision training and testing. The extent of a paraoptometrist's duties depend greatly on the size of the practice.

The majority of optometric technicians and assistants are employed in the offices of opticians. Some other work settings include eye clinics, HMOs, and optical stores. Both full-time and part-time positions exist for these workers, and full-time employees typically work at least 40 hours a week.

Education: Training for paraoptometrists may be either on the job or through a formal training program. Assistant programs generally last a year in length and may be offered by community colleges and technical schools. Technician programs award an associate's degree and run up to two years in length. Some community colleges, as well as schools of optometry, offer these programs. The National Paraoptometric Registry certifies individuals as either OptAR or OptTR after completion of the necessary training and experience in the field.

Salary, Future Outlook: In health care today, the trend of shifting job responsibility to less expensive workers will undoubtedly lead to an increased demand for experienced optometric assistants and technicians. The optometric field in general will expand as more elderly and middle aged individuals need eye care and corrective lenses. As optometrists expand their practices, paraoptometrists will be relied upon to not only manage the office but to also assume some more of the common patient care tasks.

Index: *American Optometric Association*

ORTHOPTIST

Description: Orthoptists, under an ophthalmologist's supervision, evaluate and treat crossed eyes in children and adults. They teach patients through special exercises to coordinate the use of their eyes and may also assist with visual field or glaucoma testing. Physicians generally refer a child to an orthoptist if corrective surgery and specialized eyeglasses have not cured the focusing problem. Orthoptics has been practiced in this country for only a short time, but has proven to be a useful addition to ophthalmic medicine. Many opthalmic technologists are also certified orthoptists.

Orthoptists often work directly in an opthalmologist's office or in a hospital's ophthalmology department. Eye clinics and children's health clinics often hire orthoptists as well, and there are opportunities in research and academic institutions. Most orthoptists work full-time and may incorporate weekend or evening hours into their schedule.

Education: Presently, there are less than 20 clinics in the United States that offer training programs in orthoptics. These programs are generally two years in length. The American Orthoptic Council not only accredits these training programs but also certifies individuals who successfully graduate and pass the examination. On an annual basis, many orthoptists choose to pursue continuing education credits to keep them abreast of changes in the field.

Salary, Future Outlook: The future for orthoptists is bright primarily because the small number of training programs graduate so few new workers each year. Therefore, the demand for experienced orthoptic professionals will be far greater than the number of workers qualified to meet this demand.

Index: *American Orthoptic Council*

HEALTH CAREERS IN THE ARMED FORCES

Description: The United States Armed Forces is the largest employer in our country. Comprising the Army, Air Force, Navy, Marine Corps, and in wartime, the Coast Guard, the armed forces are our nation's defenders. Although retained particularly for times of combat, military personnel receive career training similar to that of civilians. Of the more than 2,000 occupational specialties currently available to members of the armed forces, more than 75% of them are civilian careers. The specialty training that enlisted personnel receive more than adequately qualifies them to practice in their career field after leaving the military. Health-related careers are among those for which the military offers extensive training. The professions which qualify one for the rank of medical officer include: *physician, dentist, optometrist, nurse, therapist, veterinarian,* and *pharmacist.* Other enlisted health care providers include *medical laboratory technicians, medical technologists, radiologic technologist, emergency medical technicians, dental assistants, optical assistants, pharmaceutical assistants,* and *veterinary assistants.* Often, these health professionals simply need to acquire registration or certification upon leaving the military to practice as a civilian.

Health care providers in the military are still required to follow all of the regulations mandated by the armed forces. Enlisted personnel may be stationed to serve anywhere in the world and possibly even at sea. These workers may be assigned to military hospitals, sea-bound vessels, a clinic in an under-served foreign country, or in a laboratory. During peace time, the standard work day is eight hours. In wartime periods however, hours may be erratic and the working conditions dangerous or even life-threatening. Those who enter the military must agree to serve for a specified number of years, an obligation that is legally binding.

Today, enlisted members of the military are volunteers who typically serve eight years of combined active duty and reserve work. Recruited individuals must pass a physical examination and a written Armed Services Vocational Aptitude Battery test to be accepted into the armed forces. Once enlisted, they undergo a two to three month "basic" training period which prepares them for the rigors of a life in the military. Occupational training programs last from ten weeks to a year and are offered in numerous health disciplines. The Uniformed Services University of Health Sciences offers free medical training in return for up to seven years of service in the military or Public Health Service. These individuals are automatically assigned the rank of officer.

Education: Military salaries are based on rank and the number of years in the service. In 1995, military personnel on average earned $29,300, while officers averaged $52,800. Often, the base salary is less than that earned by civilian workers of the same specialty. However, the military provides free room and board, free medical and dental care, an allowance for military clothing, privileges in discounted military shopping centers, travel opportunities, and 30 days of paid vacation a year. For those interested in a health profession, enlistment allows them to avoid the steep debts of graduate school and still receive excellent training. Members of the armed forces seeking additional education are eligible for financial reimbursement under the New Montgomery GI Bill.

Salary, Future Outlook: Due to the military downsizing, many branches of the armed forces have significantly reduced their numbers of enlisted personnel. Today, however, numbers are expected to remain stable, barring any military insurrection. Increasingly, the military will look to recruit new members with some years of study beyond high school or some advanced skills. For many health care professionals, a career in the armed forces will continue to be a stable and advantageous option. In addition to the financial advantages that this option entails, these individuals also will be exposed to the most advanced medical procedures and scientific equipment of our time.

As stated throughout this publication, the health care industry is currently in a state of change. This change goes beyond the administrative level, however. Today, more and more people are adopting alternative strategies to traditional medical care. Many of these alternative medicine regimens date back thousands of years and stem from cultural beliefs of spirituality and healing. By relying on the medicinal value of natural substances, focusing on the body as a holistic entity capable of self-healing, and avoiding conventional drug and surgical treatments, these alternative therapies appeal to the skeptics and doubters of traditional medicine. In recent years, the public appeal of these alternative health treatments has grown primarily due to convincing patient testimonials on their success. Additionally, as many of these therapies rely on a preventive approach to health care, patients find that they are able to avoid costly medical bills in the long run.

Originally shunned by traditional health care providers, alternative medicine approaches to health care are gaining legitimacy from established members of the health care field. A portion of our country's medical schools now offer course work in alternative medicine and many more medical practitioners are incorporating some nontraditional techniques into their own practices. There are many different approaches included under the broad heading of alternative medicine, each having their own code of beliefs and treatment techniques. This section covers some of the more common fields in nontraditional health care today. Because the renewed interest in these fields is very recent, more comprehensive and extensive career information is not yet available.

ACUPRESSURE

Description: An ancient Chinese therapy that dates back 5,000 years, acupressure involves the application of firm pressure by the hands to alleviate pain and tension. By focusing on specific points of the body where muscular tension is usually centered, accupressurists not only relieve immediate discomfort, but also eliminate future health problems that these tensions may initiate. This therapy helps relieve the unhealthy effects of poor diet, lack of exercise, substance abuse, and emotional stress. It is often used effectively to treat headaches and muscular discomfort. Related techniques are *Jin Shin, Shiatsu, Acu-Yoga*, and *Do-In*.

Education: The Acupressure Institute in California offers training at many levels. To be certified in massage basic training, a 150-hour program is available that covers basic principles and techniques. An additional 200-hour accupressure specialization program is available for those interested in specializing in sports acupressure, emotional balancing, women's health issues, arthritis and pain relief, advanced shiatsu programs, or traditional Asian Therapy. For individuals interested in teaching acupressure, an 850-hour advanced training program will qualify students to be instructors of acupressure techniques. Other institutions may offer training in this area, and one should contact any local accupressure institute for more information.

ACUPUNCTURE

Description: This therapy is more than 2,000 years old and was first practiced by Eastern cultures. Acupuncturists locate specific points on the body where nerves are centered, and stimulate them with very fine needles. These areas on the skin seem to directly affect underlying organs either by releasing endorphins, neurotransmitters, and prostaglandins, or by affecting the circulatory and nervous systems. Acupuncture has been used successfully to treat headaches, arthritis, anxiety disorders, substance addictions, and a variety of other health problems. It has also been used successfully in weight reduction and smoking cessation programs.

In 1997, a consensus statement released by the National Institutes of Health said there was clear evidence that needle acupuncture treatment is effective for postoperative and chemotherapy nausea and vomiting, nausea of pregnancy, and postoperative dental pain.

Education: One must either be a medical doctor or a licensed doctor of acupuncture to practice in most states. The National Accreditation Commission of Schools and Colleges for Acupuncture and Oriental Medicine (NAC-SCAOM) accredits schools of acupuncture. Today, 33 institutions are part of the Council of Colleges of Acupuncture and Oriental Medicine (CCAOM) and most programs last from three to four years. Most of these master's programs cover traditional medical topics as well as the fundamental principles of Asian medicine. Also included is an internship which offers students exposure to the field.

MASSAGE THERAPY

Description: A very popular technique today, massage therapy is used to reduce stress, complement athletic performance, lower blood pressure, improve circulation, and positively affect one's emotional and mental well being. Massage therapy dates back over 3,000 years and has its roots in Eastern and Western traditions. Massage techniques have been shown to effectively diminish pain associated with old age, cancer, PMS, and the lower back. Increasingly, employers are noticing the benefits of massage on their workers and are sponsoring work site massage sessions. Massage therapy is currently being practiced in fitness centers, private clinics, spas, cruise ships, and in clients' homes.

While massage therapy is an inherent part of some foreign health care systems and is sometimes even covered by national health insurance plans, it has not yet reached that status in the United States. It does continue however, to be one of the most popular forms of alternative medicine. Some therapies that rely on massage techniques include *craniosacral therapy, myofascial release, reflexology, shiatsu, sports massage*, and *Swedish massage.*

Education: The American Massage Therapy Association recognizes more than 60 programs that fulfill accreditation requirements. These programs must consist of at least 500 instructional hours in such topics as massage theory and technique, anatomy and physiology, and basic medical principles. The National Certification Board for Therapeutic Massage and Bodywork (NCBTMB) conducts the certification examination for massage therapists and awards a certification status (CMT-certified massage therapist) that is valid for four years of practice. Currently, 21 states have licensing requirements and officially recognize massage therapists as health care professionals with the title of LMT-licensed massage therapist.

NATUROPATHIC MEDICINE

Description: Naturopathic physicians practice homeopathic medicine, which is reliant on natural remedies, and use manipulative techniques and Asian medicine to treat the body. These physicians are general practitioners who are trained in the healing properties of proper nutrition, botanical medicine, and stress management. They treat the patient holistically and believe in preventive strategies in health care. This profession is only 100 years old and reached its peak in popularity around the 1940s and 1950s. Today, the public is again regaining interest in naturopathic medicine as an alternative to traditional health care practices.

Education: There are currently two accredited colleges of naturopathic medicine in this country. Both are four years in length and include a standard medical education in addition to training in the natural therapies. The Council on Naturopathic Medical Education is the accrediting body for these institutions. Upon graduation, students receive a Doctor of Naturopathic Medicine (ND) degree and are also recognized by the initials NMD — Naturopathic Medical Doctor. Oregon recognizes naturopathic physicians as primary care providers, which entitles them to perform the same type of procedures as traditional medical doctors. Other states have licensing boards which determine the regulations governing doctors of naturopathic medicine.

Description: These fields are by no means the only forms of alternative medicine currently being practiced in the United States. *Aromatherapists* rely on natural herbs, oils, and plants to therapeutically treat swelling, infection, depression, and a host of other ailments. *Ayruvedic Medicine* comes from India and is characterized by the fundamental belief in holistic medicine and treatment of the entire body. *Biofeedback therapy* allows an individual to consciously rid the body of stress and tension by controlling the symptoms that they see documented on electronic instruments. *Reiki* is a technique which is based on the premise that by focusing on the body, mind, spirit and internal energy of the patient, one may provide pain relief, relaxation, and happiness.

While many members of the medical community are still not comfortable with with the idea of these alternative medicine strategies, the future looks bright for skilled practitioners in these fields. Skeptics argue that these techniques are more psychosomatic than physical, and that reported episodes of healing have no medical justification. Nevertheless, many patients using these therapies are indeed feeling better. For them, relief from suffering is all that matters. Within the past century we have already seen some practices that were once considered "alternative" become main staples of the health care industry, including chiropractic medicine, osteopathic medicine, and physical therapy. However, one may only speculate whether these newer alternative medicine trends will gain similar credibility.

Index: *Acupressure Institute, American Association of Professional Hypnotherapists, American Colleges of Acupuncture and Oriental Medicine, American Massage Therapy Association, American Naturopathic Medical Association, Council of Colleges of Acupuncture and Oriental Medicine, National Certification Board for Therapeutic Massage and Bodywork, National Certification Commission for Acupuncture and Oriental Medicine, Ohashi Institute.*

ABHES - Accrediting Bureau of Health Education Schools
ABMS - American Board of Medical Specialists
ACBSW - Academy of Certified Baccalaureate Social Workers
ACSW - Academy of Certified Social Workers
ADN - Associate Degree in Nursing
ADTR - Academy of Dance Therapists Registered
AHIMA - American Health Information Management Association
AMT - American Medical Technologists
ARRT - American Registry of Radiologic Technologists
ART - Accredited Record Technician
ASCP - American Society of Clinical Pathologists
ASPH - Association of Schools of Public Health
ATR - Art Therapist, Registered

BMET - Biomedical Equipment Technician
BSN - Bachelor of Science Degree in Nursing
BSW - Bachelor's Degree in Social Work

CAAHEP - Commission of Accreditation of Allied Health Education Programs
CCAOM - Council of Colleges of Acupuncture and Oriental Medicine
CCC - Certificate of Clinical Competence
CCS - Certified Coding Specialist
CMT - Certified Massage Therapist
CNM - Certified Nurse-Midwife
CNS - Clinical Nurse Specialist
CO - Certified Orthotist
COA - Certified Ophthalmic Technician
COMT - Certified Ophthalmic Medical Technologist
CP - Certified Prosthetist
CPO - Certified Prosthetist/Orthotist
CRNA - Certified Registered Nurse Anesthetist
CRRT - Certified Respiratory Therapy Technician
CST - Certified Surgical Technologist
CT - Cytotechnologist

DAT - Dental Admissions Test
DC - Doctor of Chiropractic
DDS - Doctor of Dental Surgery
DMD - Doctor of Dental Medicine
DO - Doctor of Osteopathic Medicine
DPM - Doctor of Podiatric Medicine
DSW - Doctor of Social Work

DTR - Dietetic Technician, Registered
DTR - Dance Therapist, Registered
DVM - Doctor of Veterinary Medicine

ECG or EKG - Electrocardiograph Technician
EMT-B - Emergency Medical Technician - Basic
EMT-I - Emergency Medical Technician - Intermediate
EMT-P - Emergency Medical Technician - Paramedic

HMO - Health Maintenance Organization
HT - Histologic Technicians
HTL - Histotechnologists
HTM - Master Horticulture Therapist
HTR - Horticultural Therapist Registered

ICC - International Certification Commission for Clinical Engineering and Biomedical Technology

JCAHCO - Joint Commission on Accreditation of Health Care Organizations
JCAHPO - Joint Commission on Allied Health Personnel in Ophthalmology

LMT - Licensed Massage Therapist
LPN - Licensed Practical Nurse
LVN - Licensed Vocational Nurse

MCAT - Medical College Admission Test
MCO - Managed Care Organization
MD - Doctor of Medicine
MLS - Master's Degree in Library Science
MLT - Medical Laboratory Technician
MPH - Master's in Public Health
MRI - Magnetic Resonance Imaging Technologist
MSW - Master's Degree in Social Work
MT - Medical Technologist

NACSCAOM - National Accreditation Commission of Schools and Colleges for Acupuncture and Oriental Medicine
NATA - National Athletic Training Association
NCBTMB - National Certification Board for Therapeutic Massage and Bodywork
ND - Doctor of Naturopathic Medicine
NMD - Naturopathic Medical Doctor
NP - Nurse Practitioner

OD - Doctor of Optometry
OAT - Optometry Admissions Test
OptAR - Registered Optometric Assistant
OptTR - Registered Optometric Technician
OT - Occupational Therapist
OTA - Occupational Therapy Assistant

PA - Physician Assistant
PA-C - Physician Assistant-Certified
Pharm.D. - Doctor of Pharmacy
PMAC - Podiatric Medical Assistant Certified
Psy.D. - Doctor of Psychology
PT - Physical Therapist
PTA - Physical Therapy Assistant

QCSW - Qualified Clinical Social Worker

RBP - Registered Biologic Photographer
RD - Registered Dietitian
RDH - Registered Dental Hygienist
RMT - Registered Music Therapist
RN - Registered Nurse
RPT - Registered Phlebotomy Technician
RRA - Registered Record Administrator
RRT - Registered Respiratory Therapist

VHA - Voluntary Health Agency

	Training School & Programs	Financial Aid Programs	Job Listings	Organizational Newsletter or Subscription	Contacts In the Field	Reference Sources of Information	Volunteer/ Internship Information	Minority Statistics or Special Programs
Acupressure Institute	■		■		■	■	■	
Agency for Health Care Policy and Research			■	■		■		■
Alliance of Cardiovascular Professionals	■		■	■				
American Academy of Family Physicians	■		■	■		■	■	■
American Academy of Nurse Practitioners	■	■		■	■	■		
American Academy of Nutrition-College of Nutrition	■	■				■		
American Academy of Ophthalmology	■		■	■	■	■	■	

Acupressure Institute
1533 Shattuck Avenue
Berkeley, CA 94709
Phone: 510-845-1059
Fax: 510-845-1496
E-mail: gach@acupressure.com
Internet: http://healthy.net/acupressure

Agency for Health Care Policy and Research
2101 E. Jefferson Street
Rockville, MD 20852
Phone: 301-594-1449
Fax: 301-594-0154
Internet: http://www.ahcpr.gov

Alliance of Cardiovascular Professionals
910 Charles Street
Fredricksburg, VA 22401
Phone: 540-370-0102
Fax: 540-370-0015
E-mail: seanmce@aol.com
Internet: http://www.augusta.net/atlantic/ascp/ascpscm.html

American Academy of Family Physicians
888 D Ward Parkway
Kansas City, MO 64114
Phone: 1-800-274-2237
       816-333-9700
Fax: 816-822-9715
E-mail: fp@aafp.org
Internet: http://www.aafp.org

American Academy of Nurse Practitioners
P.O. Box 12846
Austin, TX 78711
Phone: 512-442-4262
Fax: 512-442-6469
E-mail: admin@aanp.org
Internet: http://www.aanp.org

American Academy of Nutrition-College of Nutrition
1212 Kenesaw Avenue
Sequoyah Hills Center
Knoxville, TN 37919-7736
Phone: 1-800-290-4226
       423-524-8079
Fax: 423-524-1692
E-mail: aantn@aol.com

American Academy of Ophthalmology
P.O. Box 7424
San Francisco, CA 94120
Phone: 415-561-8500
Fax: 415-561-8533
E-mail: pimr@aao.org
Internet: http:\\www.eyenet.org

	Training School & Programs	Financial Aid Programs	Job Listings	Organizational Newsletter or Subscription	Contacts In the Field	Reference Sources of Information	Volunteer/ Internship Information	Minority Statistics or Special Programs
American Academy of Pediatrics						■		

141 North Point Blvd.
Elk Grove, IL 60007
Attn: Pediatric Career Information
Phone: 847-228-5005
Fax: 847-228-5097
E-mail: kidsdocs.@aap.org
Internet: http://www.aap.org

	Training School & Programs	Financial Aid Programs	Job Listings	Organizational Newsletter or Subscription	Contacts In the Field	Reference Sources of Information	Volunteer/ Internship Information	Minority Statistics or Special Programs
American Academy of Physician Assistants	■	■	■	■	■			■

950 N. Washington Street
Alexandria, VA 22314-1552
Phone: 703-836-2272
Fax: 703-684-1924
E-mail: aapa@aapa.org
Internet: http://www.aapa.org

	Training School & Programs	Financial Aid Programs	Job Listings	Organizational Newsletter or Subscription	Contacts In the Field	Reference Sources of Information	Volunteer/ Internship Information	Minority Statistics or Special Programs
American Art Therapy Association	■	■		■	■	■		■

1202 Allanson Road
Mundelein, IL 60060
Phone: 847-949-6064
Fax: 847-566-4580
E-mail: estygariii@aol.com
Internet: http://www.arttherapy.org

	Training School & Programs	Financial Aid Programs	Job Listings	Organizational Newsletter or Subscription	Contacts In the Field	Reference Sources of Information	Volunteer/ Internship Information	Minority Statistics or Special Programs
American Association of Anatomists	■		■	■				■

9650 Rockville Pike
Bethesda, MD 20814-3998
Phone: 301-571-8314
Fax: 301-571-0619
E-mail: exec@anatomy.org
Internet: http://www.anatomy.org/anatomy/

	Training School & Programs	Financial Aid Programs	Job Listings	Organizational Newsletter or Subscription	Contacts In the Field	Reference Sources of Information	Volunteer/ Internship Information	Minority Statistics or Special Programs
American Association of Blood Banks	■	■			■			

8101 Glenbrook Road
Bethesda, MD 20814
Phone: 301-215-6482
Fax: 301-907-6895
E-mail: education@aabb.org

	Training School & Programs	Financial Aid Programs	Job Listings	Organizational Newsletter or Subscription	Contacts In the Field	Reference Sources of Information	Volunteer/ Internship Information	Minority Statistics or Special Programs
American Association for Clinical Chemistry	■		■	■				

2101 L Street, N.W., Suite 202
Washington, D.C. 20037-1526
Phone: 1-800-892-1400
         202-857-0717
Fax: 202-887-5093
E-mail: info@aacc.org
Internet: http://www.aacc.org

	Training School & Programs	Financial Aid Programs	Job Listings	Organizational Newsletter or Subscription	Contacts In the Field	Reference Sources of Information	Volunteer/ Internship Information	Minority Statistics or Special Programs
American Association of Colleges of Osteopathic Medicine	■	■						■
American Association of Colleges of Pharmacy	■	■		■		■	■	■
American Association of Colleges of Podiatric Medicine Application Service	■	■						
American Association of Dental Schools	■	■						■
American Association for Health Education	■	■		■		■	■	
American Association of Medical Assistants	■			■				
American Association of Medical Transcriptionists				■	■	■		■

American Association of Colleges of Osteopathic Medicine
5550 Friendship Blvd., Suite 310
Chevy Chase, MD 20815-7231
Phone: 301-968-4100
Fax: 301-968-4101
E-mail: www.aacom.org
Internet: http://www.aacom.org

American Association of Colleges of Pharmacy
1426 Prince Street
Alexandria, VA 22314
Phone: 703-739-2330
Fax: 703-836-8982
Internet: http://www.aacp/org

American Association of Colleges of Podiatric Medicine Application Service
1350 Piccard Drive, Suite 322
Rockville, MD 20850-4307
Phone: 1-800-922-9266
Fax: 301-990-2807
E-mail: aacpmas@aacpm.org
Internet: http://www.aacpm.org

American Association of Dental Schools
1625 Massachusetts Avenue, N.W.
Washington, D.C. 20036-9433
Phone: 202-667-9433
Fax: 202-667-0642
E-mail: aads@aads.jhu.edu

American Association for Health Education
1900 Association Drive
Reston, VA 20191
Phone: 703-476-3437
Fax: 703-476-6638
E-mail: aahe@aahperd.org
Internet: http://www.aahperd.org/aahe/aahe.html

American Association of Medical Assistants
20 N. Wacker Drive, Suite 1575
Chicago, IL 60606
Phone: 1-800-228-2262
Internet: http://www.aama-ntl.org

American Association of Medical Transcriptionists
P.O. Box 576187
Modesto, CA 95357-6187
Phone: 209-551-0883
Fax: 209-551-9317
E-mail: aamt@sna.com
Internet: http://aamt.org/aamt

	Training School & Programs	Financial Aid Programs	Job Listings	Organizational Newsletter or Subscription	Contacts In the Field	Reference Sources of Information	Volunteer/ Internship Information	Minority Statistics or Special Programs
American Association of Nurse Anesthetists	■	■						
American Association of Occupational Health Nurses	■		■	■	■			
American Association of Orthodontists	■							
American Association of Pharmacy Technicians	■			■	■	■		
American Association of Professional Hypnotherapists	■							
American Association for Respiratory Care	■	■	■	■	■			
American Board for Certification in Orthotics and Prosthetics, Inc.	■		■	■			■	

American Association of Nurse Anesthetists

222 South Prospect Avenue
Park Ridge, IL 60068
Phone: 847-692-7050
Fax: 847-692-7137
E-mail: Marguerite_brunner@aana.ccmail.compuserve.com
Internet: http://www.aana.com

American Association of Occupational Health Nurses

50 Lenox Pointe
Atlanta, GA 30324-3176
Phone: 404-262-1162
Fax: 404-262-1165
E-mail: aaohn@aaohn.org
Internet: http://www.aaohn.org

American Association of Orthodontists

401 N Lindbergh Blvd.
St. Louis, MO 63141
Phone: 314-993-1700
Fax: 314-997-1745
E-mail: aao@worldnet.att.net
Internet: http://www.aaortho.org

American Association of Pharmacy Technicians

4646 Brompton Drive
Greensboro, NC 27407-1206
Phone: 910-275-1700
Fax: 910-275-7222

American Association of Professional Hypnotherapists

P.O. Box 29
Boones Mill, VA 24065
Phone: 540-334-3035

American Association for Respiratory Care

11030 Ables Lane
Dallas, TX 75229-4593
Phone: 972-243-2272
Fax: 972-484-2720
E-mail: info@aarc.org
Internet: http://www.aarc.org

American Board for Certification in Orthotics and Prosthetics, Inc.

1650 King Street, Suite 500
Alexandria, VA 22314
Phone: 703-836-7114
Fax: 703-836-0838
E-mail: opcertmail@aol.com
Internet: opcertmail@aol.com

	Training School & Programs	Financial Aid Programs	Job Listings	Organizational Newsletter or Subscription	Contacts In the Field	Reference Sources of Information	Volunteer/ Internship Information	Minority Statistics or Special Programs
American Board of Genetic Counseling	■							
American Chiropractic Association	■			■	■	■		
American College of Acupuncture and Oriental Medicine	■	■		■	■			
American College of Clinical Pharmacology	■					■		
American College Health Association			■	■				
American College of Health Care Administrators	■		■	■	■	■	■	
American College of Healthcare Executives	■			■	■		■	■

American Board of Genetic Counseling
9650 Rockville Pike
Bethesda, MD 20814-3998
Phone: 301-571-1825
Fax: 30-571-1885
E-mail: srobinson@abcg.faseb.org
Internet: http://www.faseb.org/genetics

American Chiropractic Association
1701 Clarendon Blvd.
Arlington, VA 22209
Phone: 1-800-986-4636
Fax: 703-243-2593
E-mail: jridgely@amerchiro.org OR aowens@amerchiro.org
Internet: http://www.amerchiro.org\ACA

American College of Acupuncture and Oriental Medicine
9100 Park West Drive
Houston, TX 77063
Phone: 713-780-9777
Fax: 713-622-8882
Internet: http://www.acaom.edu
E-mail: 12657.1730@compuserve.com

American College of Clinical Pharmacology
3 Ellinwood Court
New Hartford, NY 13413-1105
Phone: 315-768-6117
Fax: 315-768-6119
E-mail: accp1ssu@aol.com

American College Health Association
P.O. Box 28937
Baltimore, MD 21240-8937
Phone: 410-859-1500
Fax: 410-859-1510
E-mail: acha@access.digex.net
Internet: http://www.acha.org

American College of Health Care Administrators
325 S. Patrick Street
Alexandria, VA 22314
Phone: 703-739-7900
Fax: 703-739-7901
E-mail: info@achca.org
Internet: http://www.acha.org

American College of Healthcare Executives
1 N. Franklin Street, Suite 1700
Chicago, IL 60606-3491
Phone: 312-424-2800
Fax: 312-424-0023
E-mail: ache@ache.org
Internet: http://www.ache.org

	Training School & Programs	Financial Aid Programs	Job Listings	Organizational Newsletter or Subscription	Contacts In the Field	Reference Sources of Information	Volunteer/ Internship Information	Minority Statistics or Special Programs
American College of Nurse-Midwives	■			■	■	■		
818 Connecticut Avenue, N.W., Suite 900 Washington, D.C. 20006 Phone: 202-728-9860 Fax: 202-728-9897 E-mail: info@acnm.org Internet: http://www.midwife.org								
American College of Surgeons	■	■			■	■		■
55 East Erie Street Chicago, IL 60611-2797 Phone: 312-664-4050 Fax: 312-440-7014 E-mail: postmaster@facs.org Internet: http://www.facs.org								
American College of Radiology						■		
1891 Preston White Drive Reston, VA 20191 Phone: 703-648-8928 Fax: 703-391-1757 E-mail: info@acr.org Internet: http://www.acr.org								
American Dance Therapy Association	■			■	■	■	■	
2000 Century Plaza, Suite 108 10632 Little Patuxent Parkway Columbia, MD 21044-3263 Phone: 410-997-4040 Fax: 410-997-4048 E-mail: info@adta.org Internet: http://www.adta.org								
American Dental Association	■							
Commission on Dental Accreditation 211 E. Chicago Avenue Chicago, IL 60611 Phone: 312-440-4653 Fax: 312-440-2915 E-mail: hartk@ada.org Internet: http://www.ada.org								
American Dental Assistants Association	■	■		■	■			
203 N LaSalle Street Chicago, IL 60601 Phone: 312-541-1550 Fax: 312-541-1496 E-mail: ADAA1@aol.com Internet: http://members.aol.com/adaa1/index.html								
American Dental Hygienists Association	■					■		
444 N. Michigan Avenue, Suite 3400 Chicago, IL 60611 Phone: 312-440-8930 Fax: 312-440-8929 E-mail: adha@ix.netcom.com Internet: http://www.adha.org								

	Training School & Programs	Financial Aid Programs	Job Listings	Organizational Newsletter or Subscription	Contacts In the Field	Reference Sources of Information	Volunteer/ Internship Information	Minority Statistics or Special Programs
The American Dietetic Association	■	■	■	■	■		■	■
American Health Care Association		■		■	■			
American Health Information Management Association	■							
American Horticultural Therapy Association	■	■		■	■	■	■	
American Industrial Hygiene Association	■		■			■		
American Massage Therapy Association	■			■	■	■		
American Medical Technologists						■		

The American Dietetic Association
216 West Jackson Blvd.
Chicago, IL 60606-6995
Phone: 1-800-877-1600
Fax: 312-899-0008
E-mail: www.network.org
Internet: http://www.eatright.org

American Health Care Association
1201 L Street, N.W.
Washington, D.C. 20005
Phone: 202-842-4444
Fax: 202-842-3860
Internet: http://www.ahca.org

American Health Information Management Association
919 N. Michigan Avenue, Suite 1400
Chicago, IL 60611
Phone: 312-787-2672
Fax: 312-787-5926
E-mail: bobg@ahima.mhs.compuserve.com
Internet: http://www.ahima.org

American Horticultural Therapy Association
362A Christopher Avenue
Gaithersburg, MD 20879
Phone: 301-948-3010
Fax: 301-869-2397
Internet: http://www.ahta.org

American Industrial Hygiene Association
2700 Prosperity Avenue, Suite 250
Fairfax, VA 22207
Phone: 703-849-8888
Fax: 703-207-3561
E-mail: cfeheley@aiha.org
Internet: http://www.aiha.org

American Massage Therapy Association
820 Davis Street, Suite 100
Evanston, IL 60201
Phone: 847-864-0123
Fax: 847-864-1178
E-mail: info@inet.amtamassage.org
Internet: http://www.amtamassage.org

American Medical Technologists
710 Higgins Road
Park Ridge, IL 60068
Phone: 847-823-5169
Fax: 847-823-0458
E-mail: amtmail@aol.com

	Training School & Programs	Financial Aid Programs	Job Listings	Organizational Newsletter or Subscription	Contacts In the Field	Reference Sources of Information	Volunteer/ Internship Information	Minority Statistics or Special Programs
American Music Therapy Association	■	■	■	■	■	■	■	
American Naturopathic Medical Association	■			■	■	■	■	
American Nurses Association	■	■	■	■	■	■	■	■
The American Occupational Therapy Association	■							
American Optometric Association	■	■	■	■	■	■	■	■
American Orthoptic Council	■			■		■		
American Osteopathic Association	■			■	■	■	■	■

American Music Therapy Association
(National Association for Music Therapy)
8455 Colesville Road, Suite 1000
Silver Spring, MD 20901
Phone: 301-589-3300
Fax: 301-589-5175
E-mail: info@musictherapy.org
Internet: http://www.musictherapy.org

American Naturopathic Medical Association
P.O. Box 96273
Las Vegas, NV 89193
Phone: 702-897-7053
Fax: 702-897-7140
E-mail: don@anmaamerica.com
Internet: http://anma.com or http://anmaamerica.com

American Nurses Association
600 Maryland Avenue, S.W., Suite 100W
Washington, D.C. 20024-2571
Phone: 202-651-7000
Fax: 202-554-2262
Internet: http://www.nursingworld.org
E-mail: main@ana.org

The American Occupational Therapy Association
4720 Montgomery Lane
P.O. Box 31220
Bethesda, MD 20824-1220
Phone: 301-652-2682
Fax: 301-652-7711
Internet: http://www.aota.org

American Optometric Association
243 N. Lindbergh Blvd.
St. Louis, MO 63141-7881
Phone: 314-991-4100
Fax: 314-991-4101
Internet: http://www.opted.org

American Orthoptic Council
3914 Nakoma Road
Madison, WI 53711
Phone: 608-233-5383
Fax: 608-263-7694

American Osteopathic Association
142 East Ontario Street
Chicago, IL 60611
Phone: 1-800-621-1773
         312-280-5800
Fax: 312-280-3860
E-mail: osteomed@wwa.com
Internet: http://www.am-osteo-assn.org

	Training School & Programs	Financial Aid Programs	Job Listings	Organizational Newsletter or Subscription	Contacts In the Field	Reference Sources of Information	Volunteer/ Internship Information	Minority Statistics or Special Programs
American Pharmaceutical Association	■	■		■	■	■	■	
American Physical Therapy Association	■	■	■	■				■
American Podiatric Medical Association	■					■		
American Psychiatric Association			■		■	■		■
American Psychological Association	■	■		■	■	■		■
American School Health Association				■		■		
American Society for Clinical Laboratory Science						■		

American Pharmaceutical Association
2215 Constitution Avenue, N.W.
Washington, D.C. 20037
Phone: 202-429-7595
Fax: 202-628-0443
E-mail: edt@mail.aphanet.org
Internet: http://www.aphanet.org

American Physical Therapy Association
1111 North Fairfax Street
Alexandria, VA 22304
Phone: 703-684-2782
Fax: 703-684-7343
Internet: http://www.apta.org

American Podiatric Medical Association
9312 Old Georgetown Road
Bethesda, MD 20814-1621
Phone: 301-571-9200
Fax: 301-530-2752

American Psychiatric Association
1400 K Street, N.W.
Washington, D.C. 20005
Phone: 202-682-6000
Fax: 202-682-6850
E-mail: apa@psych.org
Internet: http://www.psych.org

American Psychological Association
750 First Street, N.E.
Washington, D.C. 20002-4242
Phone: 202-336-5500
Fax: 202-336-5501
E-mail: order@apa.org

American School Health Association
7263 State Route 43
P.O. Box 708
Kent, OH 44240
Phone: 330-678-1601
Fax: 330-678-4526
Internet: http://www.ashaweb.org

American Society for Clinical Laboratory Science
7910 Woodmont Avenue, Suite 530
Bethesda, MD 20814
Phone: 301-657-2768
Fax: 301-657-2909
Internet: http://www.ascls.org

	Training School & Programs	Financial Aid Programs	Job Listings	Organizational Newsletter or Subscription	Contacts In the Field	Reference Sources of Information	Volunteer/ Internship Information	Minority Statistics or Special Programs
American Society of Clinical Pathologists	■							

2100 West Harrison Street
Chicago, IL 60612
Phone: 312-738-1336
Fax: 312-738-5808
E-mail: ascp@ascp.org
Internet: http://www.ascp.org

American Society of Cytopathology	■							

Attn: CPRC Secretary
400 West 9th Street, Suite 201
Wilmington, DE 19801
Phone: 302-429-8802
Fax: 302-429-8807
E-mail: asc@cytopathology.org
Internet: http://www.cytopathology.org

American Society for Cytotechnology	■			■		■		

920 Paverstone Drive, Suite #D
Raleigh, NC 27615
Phone: 919-787-5181
Fax: 919-787-4916
E-mail: astiles@compuserve.com

American Society of Echocardiography	■							

4101 Lake Boone Trail, Suite 201
Raleigh, NC 27607
Phone: 919-787-5181
Fax: 919-787-4916
E-mail: ase@mercury.interpath.com
Internet: http://www.asecho.org

American Society of Electroneurodiagnostic Technologists	■		■					

204 West 7th Street
Carroll, IA 51401-2317
Phone: 712-792-2978
Fax: 712-792-6962
E-mail: aset@netins.net
Internet: http://www.aset.org

American Society of Health System Pharmacists	■		■		■	■		

7272 Wisconsin Avenue
Bethesda, MD 20814
Phone: 301-657-3000
Fax: 301-652-8278
Internet: http://www/ashp.org

American Society for Microbiology	■			■		■	■	■

1325 Massachusetts Avenue, N.W.
Washington, D.C. 20005
Phone: 202-737-3600
Fax: 202-942-9329
E-mail: educationresources@asmusa.org
Internet: http://www.asmusa.org

	Training School & Programs	Financial Aid Programs	Job Listings	Organizational Newsletter or Subscription	Contacts In the Field	Reference Sources of Information	Volunteer/ Internship Information	Minority Statistics or Special Programs
American Society for Pharmacology and Experimental Therapeutics	■						■	
American Society of Radiologic Technologists	■		■	■	■			
American Society of Safety Engineers	■	■	■	■	■	■	■	■
American Speech-Language Hearing Association	■	■	■	■	■	■		
American Statistical Association	■		■	■		■	■	■
American Therapeutic Recreation Association						■		
American Veterinary Medical Association	■							

American Society for Pharmacology and Experimental Therapeutics
9650 Rockville Pike
Bethesda, MD 20814-3995
Phone: 301-530-7060
Fax: 301-530-7061
E-mail: aspetinfo@faseb.org
Internet: http://www.faseb.org/aspet

American Society of Radiologic Technologists
15000 Central Avenue SE
Albuquerque, NM 87123
Phone: 505-298-4500
Fax: 505-298-5036
Internet: http://www.asrt.org

American Society of Safety Engineers
1800 E. Oakton Street
Des Plaines, IL 60018-2187
Phone: 847-768-2929
Fax: 847-768-3434
E-mail: 73244.5622@compuserve.com
Internet: http://www.asse.org

American Speech-Language Hearing Association
10801 Rockville Pike
Rockville, MD 20852
Phone: 301-897-5700
Fax: 301-571-0457
Internet: http://asha.org

American Statistical Association
1429 Duke Street
Alexandria, VA 22314-3402
Phone: 703-684-1221
Fax: 703-684-2036
E-mail: asainfo@amastat.org
Internet: http://www.amastat.org

American Therapeutic Recreation Association
P.O. Box 15215
Hattiesburg, MS 39403-5315
Phone: 601-264-3413
Fax: 601-264-3337
E-mail: admin@atra.org
Internet: http://www.atra-tr.org

American Veterinary Medical Association
1931 N. Meacham Road, Suite 100
Schaumburg, IL 60173-4360
Phone: 847-925-8070
Fax: 847-925-1329
Internet: http://www.avma.org

	Training School & Programs	Financial Aid Programs	Job Listings	Organizational Newsletter or Subscription	Contacts In the Field	Reference Sources of Information	Volunteer/ Internship Information	Minority Statistics or Special Programs
Association for the Advancement of Medical Instrumentation	■		■	■	■	■		
3330 Washington Blvd., Suite 400 Arlington, VA 22201-4598 Phone: 703-525-4890 Fax: 703-276-0793 Internet: http://www.aami.org								
Association of American Indian Physicians				■			■	■
1235 Sovereign Row, Suite C-7 Oklahoma City, OK 73108 Phone: 405-946-7072 Fax: 405-946-7651 E-mail: aaip@ionet.net Inernet: http://www.aaip.com								
Association of American Medical Colleges	■	■	■	■	■	■	■	■
2450 N Street, N.W. Washington, D.C. 20037-1126 Phone: 202-828-0400 Fax: 202-828-1123 Internet: http://www.aamc.org								
Association for Education and Rehabilitation of the Blind and Visually Impaired	■		■					
P.O. Box 22397 Alexandria, VA 22304 Phone: 703-823-9690 Fax: 703-823-9695 E-mail: aernet@laser.net								
Association of Medical Illustrators	■			■			■	
1819 Peachtree Street NE, Suite 620 Atlanta, GA 30309 Phone: 404-350-7900 Fax: 404-351-3348 E-mail: assnhq@mindspring.com Internet: http://www.medical-illustrators.org								
Association of Operating Room Nurses, Inc.	■					■		
2170 S. Parker Road, Suite 300 Denver, CO 80231-5711 Phone: 1-800-755-2676 303-755-6300 Fax: 303-750-3462 E-mail: dsmith@aorn.org Internet: http://www.aorn.org								
Association of Schools and Colleges of Optometry	■							
6110 Executive Blvd., Suite 510 Rockville, MD 20852 Phone: 301-231-5944 Fax: 301-770-1828 E-mail: admini@opted.org Internet: http://www.opted.org								

270 Ways to Put Your Talent to Work in the Health Field

	Training School & Programs	Financial Aid Programs	Job Listings	Organizational Newsletter or Subscription	Contacts In the Field	Reference Sources of Information	Volunteer/ Internship Information	Minority Statistics or Special Programs
Association of Schools of Public Health						■	■	
1660 L Street N.W., Suite 204 Washington, D.C. 20036 Phone: 202-296-1099 Fax: 202-296-1252 E-mail: info@asph.org Internet: http://www.asph.org								
Association of Surgical Technologists	■			■				
7108-C S. Alton Way Englewood, CO 80112 Phone: 303-694-9130 Fax: 303-694-9169 E-mail: ast@ast.org Internet: http://www.ast.org								
Association of University Programs in Health Administration	■							
1911 North Fort Myer Drive, Suite 503 Arlington, VA 22209 Phone: 703-524-5500 Fax: 703-525-4791 E-mail: aupha@aupha.org Internet: http://www.aupha.org								
Biological Photographic Association	■			■			■	
(Biocommunications Association) 1819 Peachtree Street NE, Suite 620 Atlanta, GA 30309 Phone: 404-351-6300 Fax: 404-351-3348 E-mail: assnhq@mindspring.com Internet: http://thebpa.org								
Biomedical Engineering Society	■							
P.O. Box 2399 Culver City, CA 90231 Phone: 310-618-9322 Fax: 310-618-1333 E-mail: bmes@netcom.com Internet: http://mecca.mecca.org/BME/BMES/society/bmeshm.html								
Commission on Accreditation of Allied Health Education Programs	■							
35 East Wacker Drive, Suite 1970 Chicago, IL 60601-2208 Phone: 312-553-9355 Fax: 312-553-9616 Internet: http://www.caahep.org								
Council on Chiropractic Education	■							
7975 North Hayden Road, Suite A 210 Scottsdale, AZ 85258 Phone: 602-443-8877 Fax: 602-483-7333 E-mail: cceoffice@aol.com								

	Training School & Programs	Financial Aid Programs	Job Listings	Organizational Newsletter or Subscription	Contacts In the Field	Reference Sources of Information	Volunteer/ Internship Information	Minority Statistics or Special Programs
Council of Colleges of Acupuncture and Oriental Medicine	■							
Healthcare Financial Management Association			■	■		■		
Health Sciences Communications Association	■					■		
Institute of Food Technologists	■	■	■	■	■	■		
International Society for Clinical Laboratory Technology	■					■		
Joint Commission on Allied Health Personnel in Ophthalmology	■	■	■	■	■	■	■	
Maternity Center Association	■			■		■		

Council of Colleges of Acupuncture and Oriental Medicine
1010 Wayne Avenue, Suite 1270
Silver Spring, MD 20910
Phone: 301-608-9175
Fax: 301-608-9576

Healthcare Financial Management Association
2 Westbrook Corporation Center, Suite 700
Weshchester, IL 60154
Phone: 1-800-252-4362
  708-531-9600
Fax: 708-531-0032
Internet: http://www.hfma.org

Health Sciences Communications Association
1 Wedgewood Drive, Suite 28
Jewett City, CT 06351
Phone: 860-376-5915
Fax: 860-376-6621
E-mail: hescaone@aol.com
Internet: http://www.hesca.washington.edu

Institute of Food Technologists
221 N. LaSalle Street, Suite 300
Chicago, IL 60601
Phone: 312-782-8424
Fax: 312-782-0045
E-mail: ddduxbury@ift.org
Internet: http://www.ift.org

International Society for Clinical Laboratory Technology
917 Locust Street, Suite 1100
St. Louis, MO 63101-1413
Phone: 314-241-1445
Fax: 314-241-1449
E-mail: isclt@aol.com

Joint Commission on Allied Health Personnel in Ophthalmology
2025 Woodlane Drive
St. Paul, MN 55125-2995
Phone: 612-731-2944
Fax: 612-731-0410
E-mail: jcahpo@jcahpo.org
Internet: http://www.jcahpo.org

Maternity Center Association
281 Park Avenue, 5th Floor
New York, NY 10010
Phone: 212-777-5000
Fax: 212-777-9320
E-mail: mcags@aol.com

	Training School & Programs	Financial Aid Programs	Job Listings	Organizational Newsletter or Subscription	Contacts In the Field	Reference Sources of Information	Volunteer/ Internship Information	Minority Statistics or Special Programs
Medical Library Association	■	■	■	■			■	■
National Association of Community Health Centers			■	■	■			
National Association of Dental Laboratories	■		■	■	■	■		
National Association of Emergency Medical Technicians	■				■	■		
National Association for Home Care			■	■		■		
National Association of Medical Staff Services			■	■	■	■		
National Association of Science Writers, Inc.	■	■	■	■	■			

Medical Library Association
6 North Michigan, Suite 300
Chicago, IL 60602
Phone: 312-419-9094
Fax: 312-419-8950
E-mail: info@mlahq.org
Internet: http://www.kumc.edu/mla

National Association of Community Health Centers
1330 New Hampshire Avenue, N.W., Suite 122
Washington D.C. 20036
Phone: 202-659-8008
Fax: 202-659-8519

National Association of Dental Laboratories
555 E. Braddock Road
Alexandria, VA 22314
Phone: 703-683-5236
Fax: 703-549-4788
E-mail: nadl@erols.com
Internet: http://www.nadl.org

National Association of Emergency Medical Technicians
102 W. Leake Street
Clinton, MS 39056
Phone: 601-924-7744
Fax: 601-924-7325
E-mail: naemthq@aol.com
Internet: http://www.naemt.org

National Association for Home Care
(Hospice Association of America)
519 C Street, N.E., Stanton Park
Washington, D.C. 20002-5809
Phone: 202-547-7424
Fax: 202-547-5287
Internet: http://www.nahc.org

National Association of Medical Staff Services
631 East Butterfield Road
Suite 311
Lombard, IL 60148
Phone: 630-271-9814
Fax: 630-271-0295
E-mail: namss@aol.com
Internet: http://www.namss.org

National Association of Science Writers, Inc.
P.O. Box 294
Greenlawn, NY 11740
Phone: 516-757-5664
Fax: 516-757-0069
Email: diane@nasw.org
Internet: http://www.nasw.org

	Training School & Programs	Financial Aid Programs	Job Listings	Organizational Newsletter or Subscription	Contacts In the Field	Reference Sources of Information	Volunteer/ Internship Information	Minority Statistics or Special Programs
National Association of Social Workers	■	■	■	■	■	■	■	■
National Athletic Trainers Association	■		■	■	■	■	■	■
National Certification Board for Therapeutic Massage and Bodywork				■	■			
National Certification Commission for Acupuncture and Oriental Medicine	■			■				
National Dental Association	■			■				
National Environmental Health Association		■					■	

National Association of Social Workers
750 First Street, N.E., Suite 700
Washington, D.C. 20002
Phone: 202-408-8600
Fax: 202-336-8310
Internet: http://www.naswdc.org

National Athletic Trainers Association
2952 Stemmons Freeway
Dallas, TX 75247
Phone: 1-800-879-6282
        214-637-6282
Fax: 214-637-2206
Internet: http://www.nata.org

National Certification Board for Therapeutic Massage and Bodywork
8201 Greensboro Drive, Suite 300
McLean, VA 22102
Phone: 703-610-9015
Fax: 703-610-9005
E-mail: cke@ncbtmb.com
Internet: http://www.ncbtmb.com

National Certification Commission for Acupuncture and Oriental Medicine
11 Canal Center Plaza, Suite 300
Alexandria, VA 22314
Phone: 703-548-9004
Fax: 703-548-9079
E-mail: ncca@compuserve.com
Internet: http://www.nccaom.org

National Dental Association
5506 Connecticut Avenue, N.W.,
Suite 24
Washington, D.C. 20015
Phone: 202-244-7555
Fax: 202-244-5992
Internet: http://www.natdent.org

National Environmental Health Association
720 S. Colorado Blvd.
South Tower, Suite 970
Denver, CO 80246
Phone: 303-756-9090
Fax: 303-691-9490
E-mail: neha.org@juno.com
Internet: http://www.neha.org/~beckyr

	Training School & Programs	Financial Aid Programs	Job Listings	Organizational Newsletter or Subscription	Contacts In the Field	Reference Sources of Information	Volunteer/ Internship Information	Minority Statistics or Special Programs
National Federation of Licensed Practical Nurses, Inc.	■			■	■			■
National League for Nursing	■	■		■		■		
National Medical Fellowships, Inc.		■		■				■
National Optometric Association					■			■
National Organization for Human Service Education	■	■	■	■	■	■	■	
National Rehabilitation Counseling Association						■		
National Society of Genetic Counselors	■			■	■			

National Federation of Licensed Practical Nurses, Inc.
1418 Aversboro Road
Garner, NC 27529
Phone: 1-800-948-2511
    919-779-0046
Fax: 919-779-5642
E-mail: cbarbour@ntwrks.com. OR jbeal@ntwrks.com
Internet: http://www.nflpn.com

National League for Nursing
350 Hudson Street
New York, NY 10014
Phone: 212-989-9393
Fax: 212-989-2272
Internet: http://www.nln.org

National Medical Fellowships, Inc.
110 W. 32nd Street, 8th Floor
New York, NY 10001-3205
Phone: 212-714-0933
Fax: 212-239-9718

National Optometric Association
3723 Main Street, P.O.Box F
East Chicago, IN 46312
Phone: 219-398-1832
Fax: 219-398-1077

National Organization for Human Service Education
Brookdale Community College
765 Newman Springs Road
Lyncroft, NJ 07738-1507
Phone: 908-224-2546
Fax: 908-224-2182

National Rehabilitation Counseling Association
8807 Sudley Road, Suite 102
Manassas, VA 20110
Phone: 703-361-2077
Fax: 703-361-2489
E-mail: nrcaoffice@aol.com

National Society of Genetic Counselors
233 Canterbury Drive
Wallingford, PA 19086-6617
Phone: 610-872-7608
Fax: 610-872-1192
E-mail: nsgc@aol.com
Internet: http://members.aol.com/nsgcweb/nsgchome.htm

	Training School & Programs	Financial Aid Programs	Job Listings	Organizational Newsletter or Subscription	Contacts In the Field	Reference Sources of Information	Volunteer/ Internship Information	Minority Statistics or Special Programs
National Society for Histotechnology	■			■	■	■		
4201 Northview Drive, Suite 502 Bowie, MD 20716-2604 Phone: 301-262-6221 Fax: 301-262-9188 E-mail: histo@nsh.org Internet: http://www.nsh.org								
Ohashi Institute	■				■			
12 West 27th Street New York, NY 1001 Phone: 1-800-810-4190 Fax: 212-447-5819 E-mail: ohashiinst@aol.com Internet: http://www.ohashi.com								
Opticians Association of America	■		■	■		■		
10341 Democracy Lane Fairfax, VA 22030-2521 Phone: 1-800-443-8997 703-691-8355 Fax: 703-691-3929 E-mail: oaa@opticians.org Internet: http://www.oaa.org								
Prevent Blindness America	■							
500 East Remington Road Schaumburg, IL 60173 Phone: 1-800-331-2020 Fax: 847-843-8458 E-mail: info@preventblindness.org Internet: http://www.preventblindness.org								
Society of Diagnostic Medical Sonographers	■	■	■			■		
12770 Coit Road, Suite 408 Dallas, TX 75251-1314 Phone: 972-239-7367 Fax: 972-239-7378 E-mail: sdms@sdms.org Internet: http://www.sdms.org								
Society for Nutrition Education				■		■		
2850 Metro Drive, Suite 416 Minneapolis, MN 55425-1412 Phone: 612-854-0035 Fax: 612-854-7869 E-mail: lansi001@gold.tc.umn.edu								
Society of Nuclear Medicine	■				■	■		
1850 Samuel Morse Drive Reston, VA 22090 Phone: 703-708-9000 Fax: 703-708-9015 Internet: http://www.snm.org								

ALPHABETICAL INDEX